Framework SCIENCE

Revision Workbook

Philippa Gardom Hulme

OXFORD
UNIVERSITY PRESS

Great Clarendon Street, Oxford OX2 6DP

Oxford University Press is a department of the University of Oxford.
It furthers the University's objective of excellence in research, scholarship,
and education by publishing worldwide in

Oxford New York

Auckland Cape Town Dar es Salaam Hong Kong Karachi
Kuala Lumpar Madrid Melbourne Mexico City Nairobi
New Delhi Shanghai Taipei Toronto

With offices in

Argentina Austria Brazil Chile Czech Republic France
Greece Guatemala Hungary Italy Japan Poland Portugal
Singapore South Korea Switzerland Thailand Turkey
Ukraine Vietnam

British Library Cataloguing in Publication Data

Data available

ISBN 978-0-19-914991-9

20 19 18 17 16 15 14 13 12 11

Printed in Great Britain

Author acknowledgements
Thanks to my parents, Mary and Edward Hulme – the hours I made them spend
correcting my holiday diaries from age 7 onwards taught me to write accurately.
Many thanks to my husband, Barney Gardom, who has investigated slug
measurements, lemon batteries and hawthorn leaves in much greater detail than
the average police officer. He has also shown a previously undetected – and much
appreciated – talent for producing artwork briefs.

Contents

About this book

To parents and guardians

This book includes practically everything every student needs to fulfil their potential in the Key Stage 3 science SATs.

There is a section on each of the five key science ideas identified by the National Strategy. Also included is a section on scientific enquiry, which is now being rigorously tested in the year 9 tests.

This book is designed to be used! Students will get the most from it if they do as many of the Workout and Practice for SATs questions as they have time for. Many students will also find it helpful to highlight, colour and scribble extra notes in the Fact banks.

To students: how to use this book

This book is in six sections, with each section about one key science idea.

You can use the sections in any order – you might like to start with the one you find most interesting (or easiest) to get you off to a good start!

Each section includes:

Workout
These activities will help you find out how much you already know. Go through them on your own or with a friend – many of them are quite fun! Write your answers in the book. The first few Workout activities in each section are the easiest. If you get stuck, look for answers in the Fact bank. The index will help you to find what you need. Check your answers at the back of the book.

Fact bank
The Fact banks have nearly everything you need to know – on only 26 pages! If something is not in the Fact bank, you will probably find it in the Workout activities or Practice for SATs questions. Look in a textbook at school if there's anything else you need to find out.

Don't just read the Fact banks – highlight key points, scribble extra details in the margin or on post-it notes and make up ways to help you remember things. The messier your book is by the time you take your SATs, the better!

You could try getting a friend, or someone at home, to test you on the Fact banks. Or make cards to test yourself, with a question on one side and the answer on the other.

Concept map
These summarise each key science idea. But they're not finished – it's up to you to add details and examples. Again, use highlighters and colour to make them your own. You might like to photocopy the concept maps onto A3 so you have more space to add things.

Practice for SATs
The SATs-style questions are as much like the real thing as possible. You could work through them using the Fact bank to check things as you go, or you could do them under test conditions. As a rough guide, one mark needs about 45 seconds! The answers are in the back of the book.

In every section, level 6 and above is marked like this.

ACTIVITY A

 Fill in the empty boxes.

nutrient	what the body uses the nutrient for	foods that contain the nutrient	enzyme that breaks down molecules of the nutrient
protein			protease
carbohydrates			
fats	storing energy		
vitamins and minerals			not broken down
fibre		fruit vegetables cereals wholemeal bread	not broken down

ACTIVITY B

 Draw lines to match each bad habit to the organ (or organs) it damages. Each habit may affect more than one organ.

bad habit

organ damaged

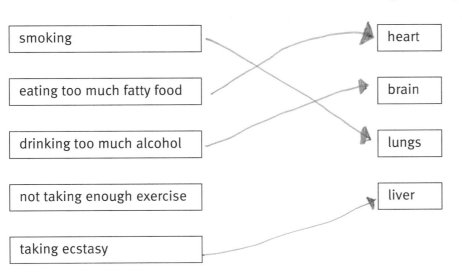

smoking

eating too much fatty food

drinking too much alcohol

not taking enough exercise

taking ecstasy

heart

brain

lungs

liver

ACTIVITY C

✎ Unscramble these words. They are all parts of the male reproductive system.

scudtremp   sitset   scrumot   heartur   spine

✎ Use your unscrambled words to label the diagram.

urethra

penis

sperm duct

testis

scvotum

✎ Each phrase in the box describes the job of one part of the male reproductive system. Write the correct letter next to each of your labels on the diagram.

P transfers sperm from testis to penis

Q sperm and urine travel down this tube

R this ejaculates semen when it is stimulated

S sperm are made here

T this holds the testes

ACTIVITY D

The substances in the box pass between a mother and an embryo.

| oxygen | nutrients | antibodies | carbon dioxide |
| waste products | some viruses | alcohol | nicotine |

✎ Write the name of each substance in the correct column of the table.

substances that pass <u>from</u> <u>the mother</u> to the embryo	substances that pass <u>from</u> <u>the embryo</u> to the mother

ACTIVITY E

In the box, write 'T' next to each true statement and 'F' next to each false statement.

1. When you breathe in, your diaphragm muscle goes down. ☐

2. Regular swimming decreases your lung volume. ☐

3. The air you breathe in contains more oxygen than the air you breathe out. ☐

4. At alveoli, oxygen goes from the blood to the air. ☐

5. Tar from cigarettes causes lung cancer. ☐

6. The air you breathe out contains less carbon dioxide than the air you breathe in. ☐

7. Having asthma can decrease your lung volume. ☐

8. When you breathe in, muscles pull your ribs up and out. ☐

9. At smokers' alveoli, carbon monoxide goes from the air to the blood. ☐

10. We have ciliated epithelial cells in our airways to help move gases in the right direction. ☐

ACTIVITY F

Use the words in the box to fill in the gaps.

protein	antibodies	bacteria	fungi	virus	yeast
transmitted	salmonella	immunisation	vaccine	antibodies	

There are three types of microbe: viruses, bacteria and _____.

Bacteria are single-celled organisms. Viruses are not cells; they are made from a piece

of genetic material with a _____ 'coat'.

Some microbes are useful, for example, _____ (a fungus) is

an ingredient of bread. Some microbes make you ill, for example the measles _____

_____ and salmonella _____.

Measles is infectious – it is _____ from person to person in

droplets from sneezing. _____ bacteria get into food –

if you eat this food, you will get food poisoning. _____ is a

way of protecting people from dangerous diseases. You are injected with a _____

_____ that contains dead or weakened microbes. Your body

makes _____ to fight the microbes. If you are infected with the

disease your body knows how to make _____ to fight it.

ACTIVITY G

✎ Draw lines to match each type of specialised cell with its function and adaptation.

function	type of cell	adaptation

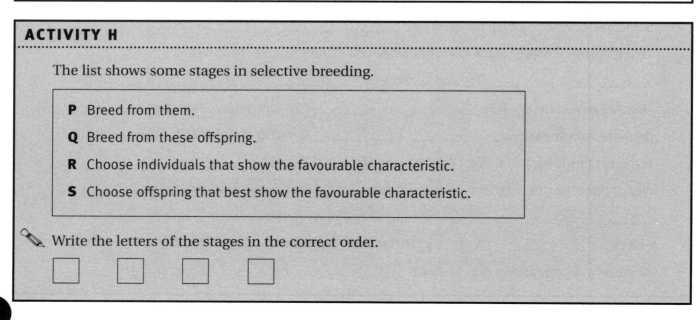

function

fertilises egg cell in plant

carries oxygen

carries genetic information from mother to offspring

protects surfaces of organs

transmits messages

type of cell

pollen cell

egg cell (ovum)

epithelial cell

red blood cell

nerve cell

adaptation

contains food store

produces lubricating liquids

conducts electrical signals

small and light

large surface area

ACTIVITY H

The list shows some stages in selective breeding.

P Breed from them.

Q Breed from these offspring.

R Choose individuals that show the favourable characteristic.

S Choose offspring that best show the favourable characteristic.

✎ Write the letters of the stages in the correct order.

☐ ☐ ☐ ☐

ACTIVITY I

Look at the data in the table. Two of the foods are pretty unusual in Britain!

Answer the questions below.

food	mass of protein in 100 g of the food, in g	mass of fat in 100 g of the food, in g
chicken	21	9
eggs	12	9
red ants	14	4
water beetles	20	8

1. Which food has the most protein in 100 g? _____

2. Which food has the least fat in 100 g? _____

3. Teenagers need to eat about 50 g of protein a day. What mass of water beetles would give a teenager all the protein she or he needs?

   _____

4. A pregnant woman needs to eat about 84 g of fat a day. What mass of eggs would give her all the fat she needed?

   _____

ACTIVITY J

Look at the words in the oval for 1 minute. Try to memorise them!

Cover up the words. Write down as many of them as you can remember.

Write down a definition of each word.

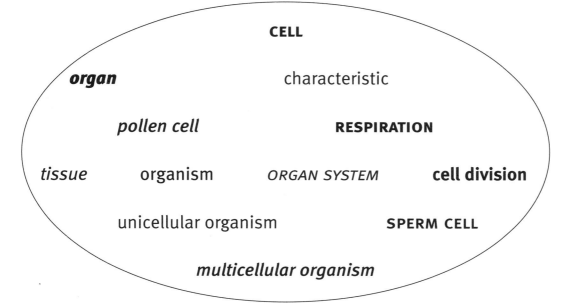

CELL

organ   characteristic

pollen cell   **RESPIRATION**

tissue   organism   *ORGAN SYSTEM*   **cell division**

unicellular organism   **SPERM CELL**

multicellular organism

Cells

What are cells?

All living things **(organisms)** are made from **cells. Unicellular organisms** are made from one cell. **Multicellular organisms** are made from many cells.

Cell structure

Most plant and animal cells contain
- a **nucleus** to control the cell
- a thin **membrane** to control what goes in and out of the cell
- a liquid **cytoplasm** where chemical reactions happen

Most plant cells also have
- a **cell wall** outside the membrane so the cell keeps its shape
- **chloroplasts** to trap light

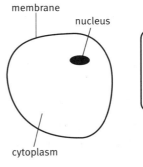

An animal cell

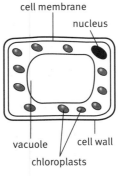

A plant cell

Specialised cells

Multicellular organisms are made of different types of cell. Each type of cell has its own function, and is adapted to carry out this function.

Type of cell	Diagram	Function (or job)	How the cell is adapted to its function
Sperm	nucleus membrane head tail	Fertilises egg cell. Carries genetic information to offspring.	Small with a tail so it can swim. Head has coating that digests egg cell membrane so sperm can get into egg cell.
Egg cell (ovum)	nucleus membrane	Fertilised by sperm. Carries genetic information.	Contains a food store so it can grow after fertilisation.
Nerve cell	cytoplasm nucleus membrane	Transmits messages around the body.	Conducts electrical signals. Very long.
Red blood cell		Carries oxygen in the blood.	Large surface area to carry as much oxygen as possible.
Ciliated epithelial cell	cilia nucleus	Protects surfaces of organs. Used to absorb or excrete substances.	Produces mucus. Joined to hair-like cilia so it has a large surface area.
Pollen cell		Fertilises egg cell in plant.	Small and light so can travel to where it's needed.

Cells, tissues and organs

- **Cells** are the building blocks of all living organisms.
- A **tissue** is a group of similar specialised cells working together.
- An **organ** is made from different tissues working together.
- An **organ system** is a group of organs working together.
- A living **organism** is a group of organ systems working together.

Growth

Organisms grow when
- cells get bigger
- cells divide and make new cells, so the number of cells increases

Photosynthesis

Photosynthesis happens in the leaves of green plants. The process makes **glucose**. Plants convert some glucose into **starch**, which they store in their leaves, roots and stems to use later. Plants also convert some glucose into **cellulose**. These processes increase the plant's **biomass**.

The raw materials for photosynthesis are **carbon dioxide** from the air and **water** from the soil. **Sunlight** is the energy source. Green **chlorophyll** absorbs sunlight.

carbon dioxide + water ⟶ glucose + oxygen

Plants need **other nutrients** to grow healthily. For example, they need nitrates to make proteins. Plants get most of these nutrients from the soil. You can add fertiliser if the soil does not contain enough of the correct nutrients.

Plant roots are adapted to taking in water and minerals from the soil by
- being spread out and branched
- being covered in root hairs so they have a large surface area
- having thin cell membranes

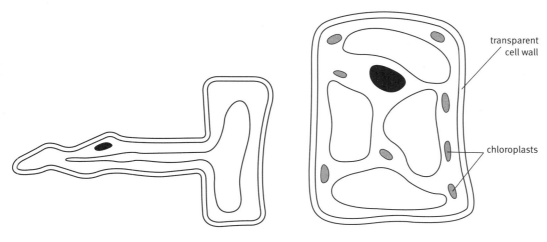

A root hair cell   *A palisade cell*

Plant **leaves are adapted to photosynthesis** by having
- big surface areas to absorb sunlight
- many chloroplasts in the cells near the top surface (chloroplasts contain chlorophyll)
- tiny holes so carbon dioxide and water particles can get in and out
- veins to transport water

Sexual reproduction

Fertilisation

Cell nuclei contain **chromosomes** that carry **genes**. Each gene is a piece of information about a **characteristic** of the organism, such as skin colour.

Fertilisation in animals and flowering plants happens when a male sex cell nucleus joins with a female sex cell nucleus. This is called **fusion**. The genes from both parents join together to make a new set of genes. The offspring will be similar to their parents, but not identical to them.

Sexual reproduction in humans

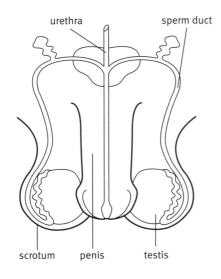

The male reproductive system

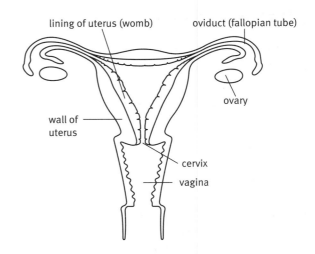

The female reproductive system

A man's testes make sperm. Sperm mix with other liquids to make **semen**. In sexual intercourse, semen travels through the man's **urethra** to the woman's **vagina**. Sperm swim up the vagina, through the uterus and into the **oviduct**. In the oviduct, one sperm might meet – and fertilise – an egg. The egg has come from one of the woman's **ovaries**. The woman is now **pregnant**.

The fertilised egg moves down the oviduct. It divides to make two, then four cells as it travels. The cells divide many more times over the next few days to make an **embryo**. The embryo fixes itself to – **implants** in – the uterus wall and continues to grow and develop. Nine weeks after fertilisation, the embryo is called a **fetus**.

The fetus gets everything it needs from its mother.

These things go **from the mother's blood to the fetus's blood** through the placenta and umbilical cord:

o nutrients
o oxygen
o antibodies to protect the embryo from disease
o alcohol, nicotine and other drugs

Waste materials go **from the fetus's blood to the mother's blood**.

Gestation periods

Human babies are born nine months after fertilisation. This is the **gestation period** for humans. Other mammals have different gestation periods. Parents look after human offspring for many years. Some animals become independent much more quickly – giraffes stand up straight after birth!

Selective breeding

Selective breeding increases the chance of certain genes passing from parent to offspring. You can use selective breeding to produce animals or plants with a certain **desirable characteristic**. If you want to breed cows that produce lots of milk, choose cows that already give lots of milk and breed from them. Their offspring will also produce lots of milk. Breed from the offspring that produce most milk.

The menstrual cycle

- **Day 1**: The lining of the uterus breaks down and blood comes out of the vagina. This is a period.
- **Day 4**: The lining of the uterus gets thicker, ready for a fertilised egg to implant.
- **Day 14**: An ovary releases an egg. The woman may get pregnant if she has intercourse.
- **Days 14–28**: The uterus lining continues to get thicker.

Respiration

Plant and animal cells need energy for every life process. In every cell, a chemical reaction called respiration **releases energy** from glucose:

glucose + oxygen ⟶ carbon dioxide + water

In animals, **blood** transports glucose and oxygen to cells. Blood carries away the waste products – carbon dioxide and water – too. This is why tissues need a good blood supply.

Circulatory system

The **heart** pumps blood round the body:
- **Deoxygenated** blood goes into the heart.
- The heart pumps this blood to the lungs to pick up oxygen.
- This **oxygenated** blood returns to the heart.
- The heart pumps this blood to every cell in the body.

Blood travels through **blood vessels**:
- **Arteries** carry blood away from the heart.
- **Veins** carry blood to the heart.
- **Capillaries** join arteries to veins. Their walls are very thin so glucose, oxygen and carbon dioxide can go through them to get into and out of cells.

Blood is a mixture of four things:
- **Red blood cells** carry oxygen and carbon dioxide.
- **White blood cells** fight disease.
- **Platelets** help blood to clot.
- **Plasma** is a liquid that nutrients, hormones and antibodies dissolve in.

Energy, nutrients and digestion

A **balanced diet** is vital for health. We must eat the right amounts of seven **nutrients**.

nutrient	why we need the nutrient	foods that contain the nutrient
protein	to grow and repair damaged tissue	meat, fish, milk, cheese, eggs, beans
carbohydrates	for energy	bread, pasta, rice, potatoes
fats	to store energy	cooking oil, butter
vitamins	for chemical reactions in the body	fruit, vegetables, cereal
minerals		milk (calcium), red meat (iron)
fibre	to help everything move around the digestive system	fruit, vegetables, cereal
water	because every chemical reaction in the body happens in water	drinks, fruit, vegetables

Digestion

All cells need nutrients. These nutrients come from food. But most food molecules are too big to be useful to cells. Digestion breaks down big, insoluble food molecules into smaller soluble molecules that cells can **absorb**.

Enzymes help to break down big nutrient molecules quickly:
o **Protease** enzymes break down **proteins** to **amino acids**.
o **Amylase** enzymes break down **carbohydrates** (like starch) to **glucose**.
o **Lipase** enzymes break down **fats** to smaller molecules.

The body cannot digest some food – this is **egested** from the anus.

The lungs and breathing

When you **inhale** (breathe in):
o Muscles pull the ribs up and out.
o The diaphragm goes down.
o Your chest volume has increased so air rushes in.

When you **exhale** (breathe out):
o The muscles between the ribs relax.
o Your diaphragm goes up.
o Air rushes out.

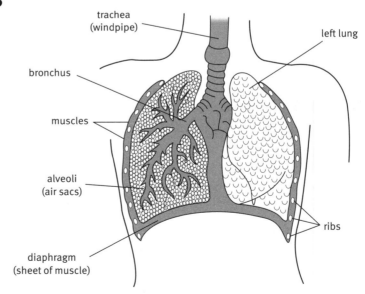

In the lungs, oxygen goes from the air to the blood and carbon dioxide goes from the blood to the air. The gases are **exchanged** in **alveoli**. Alveoli do a good job because:
o They have a **large surface area**.
o They are surrounded by **capillaries**.
o They have very **thin walls** that gas molecules can easily get through.

Micro-organisms (microbes)

microbe	what are they?	diseases	uses
bacteria	single-celled organisms	food poisoning tetanus whooping cough	making yoghurt
fungi	made from cells	athlete's foot	antibiotics making bread
viruses	a piece of genetic material with a protein 'coat'	flu chickenpox HIV/AIDS	none!

Your body defends itself against infecting microbes in many ways:
○ Your **skin** is a barrier to most microbes.
○ **Mucus** and **cilia** in your breathing system trap microbes.
○ **Stomach acid** kills most bacteria that you eat.
○ **White blood cells** make **antibodies** to destroy microbes.

Immunisation protects you from some diseases. A vaccine contains dead or weakened microbes of a certain disease. Your body makes antibodies to fight these microbes. If you are infected with the disease your body already knows how to make the antibodies it needs to fight the invading microbe.

Antibiotics stop bacteria growing in your body. They do not affect viruses.

Staying healthy

Multicellular organisms stay healthy only if all the organ systems work well together. Drugs change the way your body or mind works.

Smoking
○ **Nicotine** is addictive. It narrows blood vessels, raises blood pressure and makes the heart beat faster.
○ **Tar** causes lung cancer.
○ **Carbon monoxide** replaces some oxygen in the blood, making it difficult for cells to get enough oxygen for respiration.

Alcohol and other drugs
○ **Alcohol** slows down your reaction time, making driving dangerous.
○ It damages the liver and fetus.
○ **Illegal drugs** like heroin, cannabis and ecstasy damage the brain and other organs.

Exercise
○ Exercise makes circulation and breathing systems work more efficiently.
○ But it can damage joints (if you're not careful!).

CONCEPT MAP

Cells

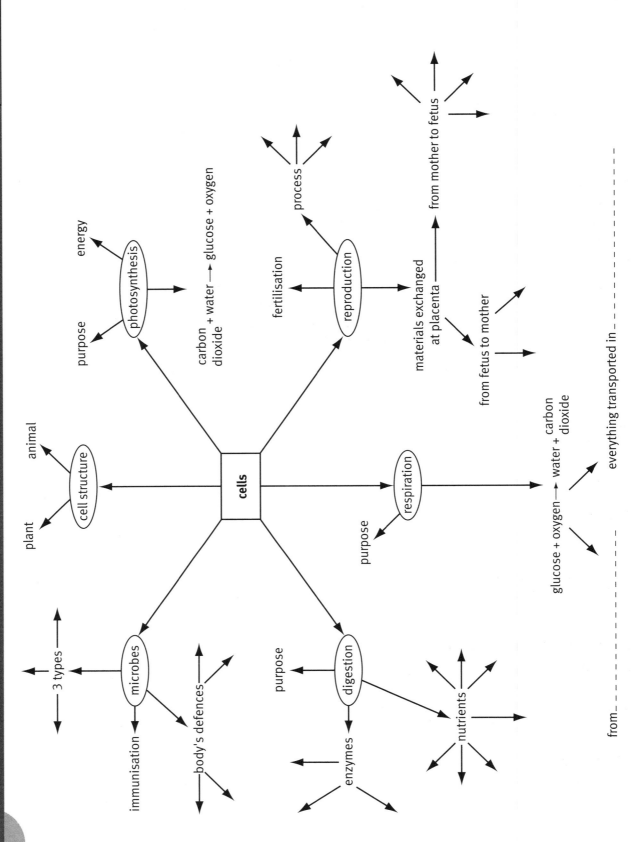

cells

cell structure
- animal
- plant

photosynthesis
- purpose
- energy

carbon dioxide + water ⟶ glucose + oxygen

reproduction
- fertilisation
- process

materials exchanged at placenta
- from mother to fetus
- from fetus to mother

respiration
- purpose

glucose + oxygen ⟶ water + carbon dioxide

everything transported in – – – – – – – – – – – –

from – – – – – – – – – – – – – – – – – –

microbes
- 3 types
- immunisation
- body's defences

digestion
- purpose
- enzymes
- nutrients

1. The diagram below shows a plant cell.

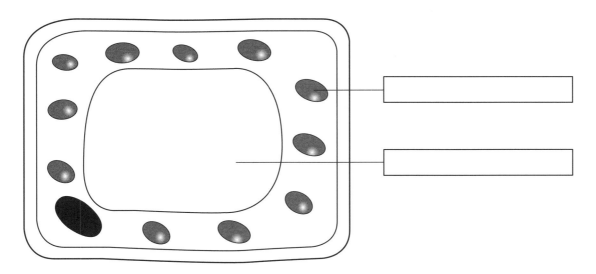

(a) (i) The lines from the boxes point to two parts of the cell.
In the boxes, write the names of these two parts. *2 marks*

(ii) Each part of the cell has a function.
Draw a straight line from the name of each part to its function.
Draw only four lines. *4 marks*

name of part of cell   **function**

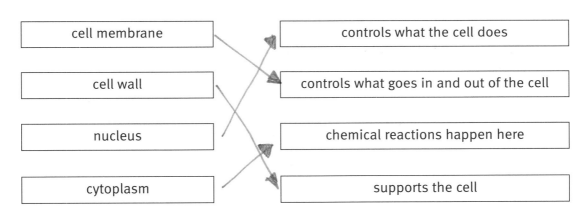

(b) Fill the **two** gaps in the sentences below. *2 marks*

All living things are made from cells. Cells join together to form

_____.

These work together in _____,

for example the heart or brain.

maximum 8 marks

2. The diagram below shows the female reproductive system.

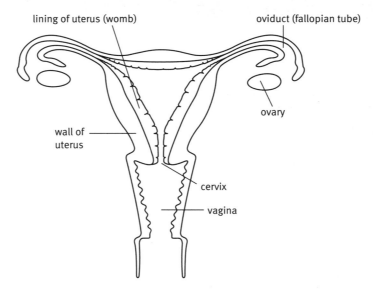

(a) (i) From which labelled part of the female reproductive system are human eggs (ova) released?

_____

1 mark

(ii) How often are eggs normally released?

_____

1 mark

(iii) Which labelled part of the female reproductive system breaks down during menstruation?

_____

1 mark

(b) (i) Name the two cells that join together at fertilisation.

_____ and _____

1 mark

(ii) In which labelled part of the female reproductive system does fertilisation normally happen?

_____

1 mark

(c) When a woman is pregnant, the fetus develops in the uterus. Substances, such as nutrients, pass from the mother's blood to the fetus's blood.

(i) Name **one other useful** substance that passes from the mother's blood to the fetus's blood.

_____

1 mark

(ii) Name **two harmful substances** that may pass from the mother's blood to the fetus's blood.

_____ and _____

2 marks

maximum 8 marks

3. The table shows the masses of nutrients in 100 g of baked beans.

nutrient	mass of nutrient in 100 g of baked beans
protein	4.2 g
carbohydrate	14.8 g
fat	0.6 g
fibre	3.3 g

(a) The label on the can claims that baked beans are **high** in protein and fibre and **low** in fat.

   (i) What do our bodies use protein for?   *1 mark*

   (ii) Calculate the mass of protein in a 400 g can of baked beans.   *1 mark*

   (iii) Which organ may be harmed if a person eats too much fat?   *1 mark*

   (iv) Adults need 18 g of fibre every day. Calculate the mass of baked beans that contains 18 g of fibre.   *2 marks*

(b) Enzymes break down big nutrient molecules in the digestive system.

   (i) Draw a straight line from the nutrient molecule to the enzyme that breaks it down. Draw only **three** lines.   *3 marks*

     nutrient molecule   **enzyme that breaks it down**

nutrient molecule	enzyme that breaks it down
protein	lipase
starch (a carbohydrate)	amylase
fat	protease

   (ii) Explain why protein, carbohydrate and fat molecules must be broken down before the body can use them.   *1 mark*

maximum 9 marks

4. Plants make glucose in a process called photosynthesis.

(a) One raw material of photosynthesis is water. Plants absorb water through their root hairs.
Describe how root hair cells are adapted to their function.

1 mark

_____

_____

(b) Photosynthesis takes place in leaves.
The drawing shows a cell from the leaf of a plant.
Describe how the leaf cell is adapted to its function.

2 marks

_____

_____

(c) Write a word equation for photosynthesis.

2 marks

_____

(d) Plant cells use the glucose that is made in photosynthesis for respiration. Respiration releases useful energy for all life processes in the green plant.

(i) One life process is growth. Name two other life processes.

2 marks

_____ and _____

(ii) What are the two waste products of respiration?

1 mark

_____ and _____

(iii) At night, plants can respire but they cannot photosynthesise.
Explain why.

1 mark

_____

maximum 9 marks

Interdependence

ACTIVITY A

 On the food web below:

- Draw a triangle round each **producer**.
- Draw a circle round each **predator**.
- Draw a square round each **primary consumer**.
- Draw a cloud round each **prey** animal.
- Underline each **herbivore**.

Some organisms on the food web will have more than one shape round them!

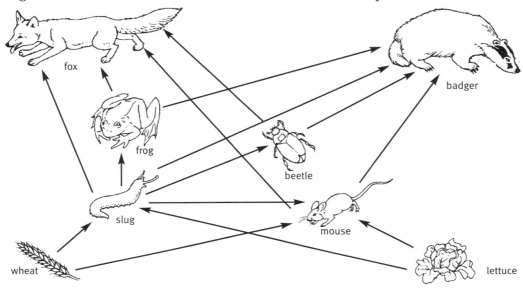

fox

badger

frog

beetle

slug

mouse

wheat

lettuce

ACTIVITY B

Fill in the gaps.

Use the food web on page 28 and the words in the box to help you.

decreases   compete   increase   decrease

If many rabbits catch a disease and die, the rabbit population will

_____. The hare population will probably

_____ because hares do not have to

_____ with so many rabbits for food. The rabbits' deaths

may mean that the badger population _____ because

badgers eat rabbits.

ACTIVITY C

 Make up 15 sentences using the phrases in the table. Each sentence must include a phrase from each column.

 Write your answers in the grid at the bottom.

For example, the sentence

Prey have eyes on the sides of their heads so they can watch for danger from all directions

becomes Y1G.

X Predators	1 have eyes on the sides of their heads	A so that they know when to run away
	2 have eyes on the front of their heads	B so that they can detect predators from far away
	3 have sharp claws, teeth or beaks	C so that they can judge distances and see moving animals well
	4 can run very fast	D so that they can detect their prey from far away
	5 are very strong	E so that they can blend into the background so that other animals cannot see them
	6 are easily startled	F so that they can escape
	7 have a good sense of smell	G so that they can watch for danger from all directions
Y Prey	8 have excellent hearing	H so that they can kill an animal
		I so that they can eat animal flesh
	9 are well camouflaged	J so that they can catch up with their prey

Y														
1														
g														

ACTIVITY D

This activity is about plant classification.

✎ Write the words from the box below in the correct spaces.

grasses	roots	rose	branched	fir tree	cones
parallel	photosynthesis	simple leaves	flowers	tree fern	flowers

plants

- make their own food by _photosynthesis_

- are multicellular

- grow

- cannot move from place to place on their own

plants that reproduce using seeds

plants that reproduce using spores

conifers

- make seeds in

  cones

- usually keep their leaves in winter

- e.g.

  fir tree

flowering plants

- make seeds in

  _____

- make fruit

mosses and liverworts

- have

  _____

  _____

- have tiny roots

dicotyledons

- broad leaves with

  _____

  veins

- _____

  often brightly coloured

- e.g.

  _____

monocotyledons

- narrow leaves with

  parallel

  veins

- flowers often small and not brightly coloured

- e.g.

  _____

ferns

- have leaves

- have

  _____

- e.g.

  tree fern

23

ACTIVITY E

 Use the clues to fill in the grid.

The vertical word is an important scientific idea.

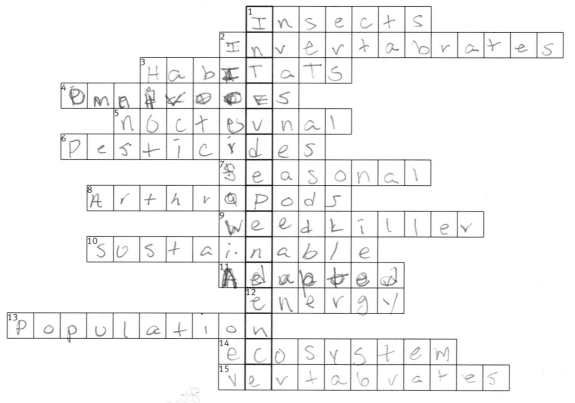

1. Ants, flies and ladybirds are all . . .

2. Animals without backbones are . . .

3. The places where organisms live are called . . .

4. Animals that eat plants and other animals are . . .

5. . . . animals have special adaptations to help them survive at night.

6. . . . kill insects and other animals that damage food crops.

7. Squirrels hibernate in winter. They are adapted to cope with . . . changes.

8. Spiders and flies are examples of . . .

9. . . . kill plants that compete with food crops.

10. The aim of . . . development is to meet people's needs today without stopping future generations meeting their needs.

11. Giraffes have long necks. They are . . . to eating leaves from treetops.

12. Food chains show how . . . is transferred from one organism to another.

13. The . . . of a species is the number of individuals of the species that live in a certain habitat.

14. The animals, plants, rocks and so on in a habitat are called an . . .

15. Fish, reptiles, birds, amphibians and mammals are all . . .

ACTIVITY F

✎ Draw lines to show what weeds and pests **compete with** and **compete for**. Each word in the 'compete with' column may be joined to more than one word in the 'compete for' column.

	compete with	**compete for**
		light
weeds	humans	space
		food
pests	crops	soil nutrients
		water

ACTIVITY G

This food chain includes a human food crop (wheat), a pest (slug) and a bird (crow):

wheat → slug → crow

Below is a pyramid of numbers for the food chain:

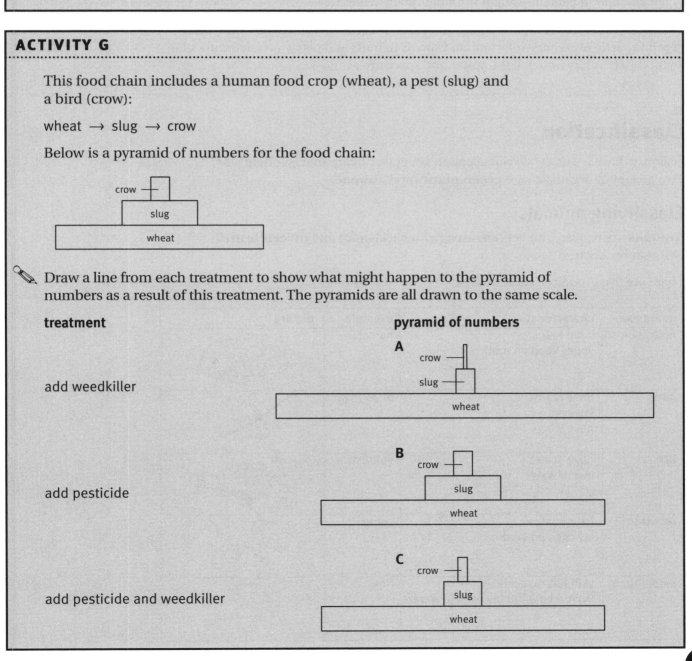

✎ Draw a line from each treatment to show what might happen to the pyramid of numbers as a result of this treatment. The pyramids are all drawn to the same scale.

treatment	pyramid of numbers
add weedkiller	**A** crow / slug / wheat
add pesticide	**B** crow / slug / wheat
add pesticide and weedkiller	**C** crow / slug / wheat

25

Species and variation

A **species** is a group of plants or animals that has very similar **characteristics**. Plants or animals of the same species can breed together to produce fertile offspring. Some examples of species are elephants, humans, robins, roses and daisies.

There is **variation** between different members of the same species. For example, elephants are not identical to each other – the height, skin colour and trunk length of one elephant are different to those of another elephant.

There are two causes of variation:
o **Inherited variation** – characteristics like hair colour, eye colour and leaf shape pass from parents to offspring through genes.
o **Environmental variation** – living conditions influence some characteristics. For example, a person's weight is influenced by what they eat.

You cannot completely separate the two causes of variation. The height of a tree depends partly on genetic information from its parents and partly on environmental factors such as how much light, water and space are available.

Classification

Scientists have a worldwide classification system for living things (organisms). Two groups of organisms are **green plants** and **animals**.

Classifying animals

Animals are divided into **vertebrates** (with backbones) and **invertebrates** (without backbones).

There are five groups of **vertebrates**.

group name	characteristics	example	picture
mammals	have hair young feed on mother's milk	hamster	
birds	have feathers lay eggs have wings	budgerigar	
fish	have scales live in water	goldfish	
reptiles	have scales lay eggs on land	cobra	
amphibians	skin has no scales live on land but lay eggs in water	frog	

There are seven groups of **invertebrates**. Two of these groups are
- **Arthropods** including insects and spiders. These have hard outer skeletons and simple eyes.
- **Molluscs** including snails. These have shells and a soft body.

Classifying green plants

You can classify **green plants** in different ways.

One classification system divides plants into
- Plants with **waxy waterproof surfaces** on their leaves, like all flowering plants.
- Plants without **waterproof surfaces**, like mosses. These plants must live in damp habitats because water escapes from their leaves very easily.

Another way of classifying plants depends on how they reproduce:
- plants that make **seeds** to reproduce, like grasses, roses and pine trees
- plants that make **spores** to reproduce, like ferns and mosses

(Workout activity D has more details about this classification system.)

Adaptation

Different **habitats** have different **features** and support different plants and animals. The plants and animals that live in one habitat depend on each other – they are **interdependent**. Plants and animals are **adapted** to make sure their species survives.

Organisms are adapted to their **environment**:
- Moles live underground.

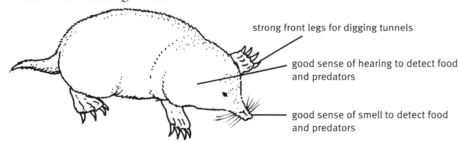

strong front legs for digging tunnels

good sense of hearing to detect food and predators

good sense of smell to detect food and predators

- Bluebells grow in woodlands. They flower before the leaves of the trees block out too much sunlight.

Organisms are adapted to **daily changes** in their habitats:
- Badgers come to city gardens at night. They have good senses of hearing and smell to find their prey (worms, small mammals and insects).
- Blackbirds are active in city gardens during the day. They have good eyesight so that they can see the worms and other small animals that they eat.

Organisms are adapted to **seasonal changes** in their habitats:
- In Britain bats are active in summer. They **hibernate** in winter because there are not enough insects for them to eat.
- In Tanzania, wildebeest **migrate** in the dry season to find enough grass to eat.

Animals are adapted to how they **feed** (and to protect themselves!):
- **Predators** have good eyesight or hearing to find their prey. They move fast and quietly to catch the prey. They have sharp beaks, teeth or claws to kill the prey.
- **Prey animals** often have eyes on the sides of their heads and good hearing to detect predators. Some have armour (like spikes) to protect them from predators.
- Giraffes eat thorny leaves from the tops of trees. They have long necks to reach the leaves. They have long muscular tongues and thick gluey saliva so the thorns don't hurt their mouths.

Food chains and webs

Food chains show **feeding relationships** in a habitat. The arrows mean 'is eaten by'. They show how energy is transferred from one organism to another. The Sun is the source of energy for all food chains.

Three grassland food chains are:

blackberry → rabbit → badger   grass → hare → fox
hawthorn → rabbit → buzzard

You can combine food chains to make a food web:

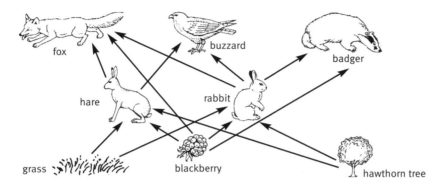

- Grass, blackberry and hawthorn are **producers**. They make food by photosynthesis.

- Hares, rabbits, foxes, buzzards and badgers are **consumers**. They cannot make their own food. Rabbits and hares are **primary consumers** – they eat producers only. Badgers, buzzards and foxes are **secondary consumers** – they eat primary consumers.

- Rabbits and hares are **herbivores**. They only eat plants.

- Buzzards are **carnivores**. They eat only animals.

- Badgers and foxes are **omnivores**. They eat plants and animals.

Population

The **population** of a species is the number of individuals that lives in a particular habitat. Population size depends on **food availability**, **predator population** and **competition**. In the food web above:

- The number of foxes depends on how much food is available. If the number of hares goes down there is less food for foxes. The fox population may decrease.

- If the buzzard population goes up then the number of rabbits may decrease. There are more buzzards to eat the rabbits.

- Hares compete with rabbits for food. If many rabbits suddenly die from disease, there are fewer rabbits to eat grass and hawthorn, so more food is available for hares. The hare population may increase.

Pyramids of numbers show the relative populations of each organism in a habitat:

Food for humans

Photosynthesis and energy

Photosynthesis is vital to humans! In photosynthesis, plants convert energy from sunlight into stored energy. We eat plants directly or eat animals that eat plants:

wheat $\longrightarrow$ human

wheat $\longrightarrow$ chicken $\longrightarrow$ human

Energy from sunlight flows through the whole system. But organisms need some of this energy for life processes – like moving and reproducing. So not all of the Sun's energy that is transferred to the wheat is available to the human or chicken that eats the wheat.

What do crops need to grow well?

○ Crops need enough water, carbon dioxide, light and space.

○ Crops need **minerals** (like nitrogen, phosphorus and potassium). Farmers add fertilisers if the soil does not have enough minerals for the crop.

Weedkillers and pesticides

Other plants – weeds – compete with food crops for water, minerals, sunlight and space. Farmers may add **weedkillers** to kill weeds, so the food crop yield increases. But the number of different plant species in the habitat decreases, so there is less **biodiversity**.

Some animals, such as insects and small mammals, damage crops. Farmers may add **pesticides** to kill these animals, so the food crop yield increases. But there may now be fewer insects for birds to eat, so bird populations decrease. There is less biodiversity.

Some weedkillers and pesticides are poisonous. They can accumulate through a food chain, so a carnivore may end up with a high concentration of a poison in its body. This is **bioaccumulation**.

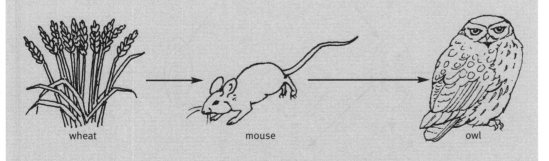

wheat   mouse   owl

A farmer sprays pesticide onto her wheat. Mice eat the wheat, and the pesticide. Owls eat many mice, so the pesticide accumulates in their bodies. Owls that have eaten the pesticide have reproductive problems and may regurgitate blood.

Sustainable development

Producing food can cause great environmental damage. **Sustainable development** aims to meet people's needs today, without stopping future generations from meeting their needs.

Interdependence

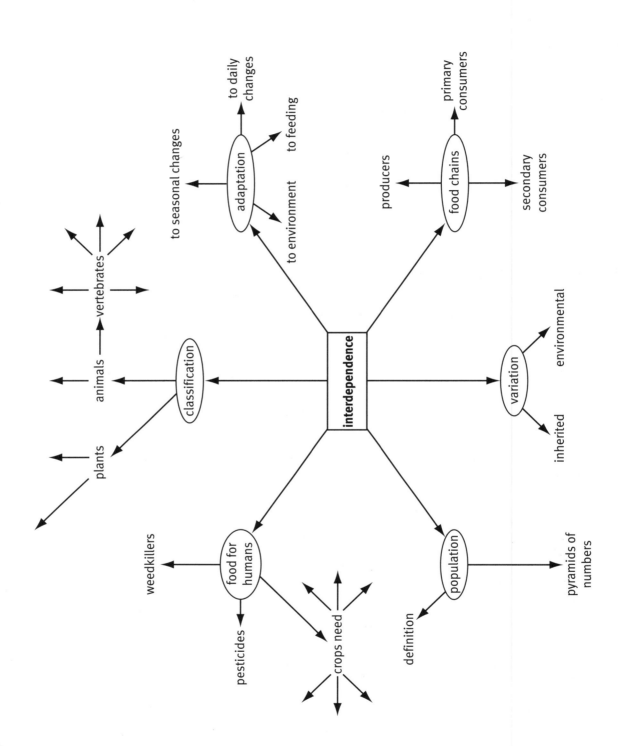

1. All the organisms in the drawing below are animals.

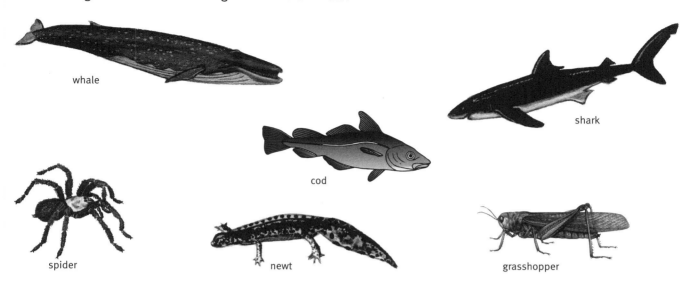

whale

shark

cod

spider   newt   grasshopper

(a) Write the names of **four** vertebrates shown in the pictures.   *4 marks*

1. _____   2. _____

3. _____   4. _____

(b) Write the names of **two** fish shown in the pictures.   *2 marks*

1. _____   2. _____

(c) Write the names of **two** arthropods shown in the pictures.   *2 marks*

1. _____   2. _____

maximum 8 marks

2. (a) Some police officers use horses to help them to
   - control crowds
   - search fields and beaches for missing people
   - meet the public

   Which **two** features would you look for when choosing a horse for the police service?
   Choose from the list in the box below.
   Write your answers on the next page. Give a reason for each choice.

   > good stamina
   > long hair
   > big feet
   > calm
   > brave
   > fast runner

1. feature _____ *1 mark*

   reason _____

   _____ *1 mark*

2. feature _____ *1 mark*

   reason _____

   _____ *1 mark*

(b) The drawing below shows a racehorse. Every individual racehorse is different.

Look at the list of characteristics in the box.

mass	eye colour	tail docked short or natural length
colour	number of instructions it understands	

For each characteristic decide whether the cause of variation is **inherited** or
environmental or a **combination of both inherited and environmental**.
Write your answers in the correct column of the table. *5 marks*

inherited	environmental	combination of both inherited and environmental

maximum 9 marks

3. The drawing below shows a food web for plants and animals that live in African grasslands.

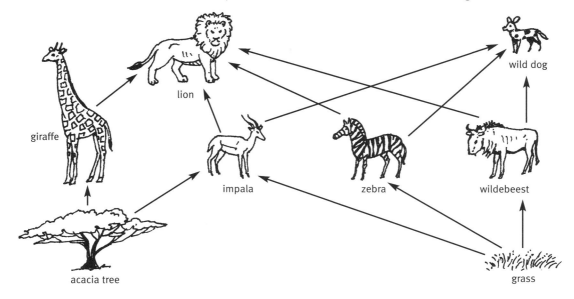

(a) From the food web, give the names of

    (i)   one producer _____   *1 mark*

    (ii) one predator _____   *1 mark*

    (iii) one prey _____   *1 mark*

    (iv) one herbivore _____   *1 mark*

(b) In the space below write **one** food chain **from the food web**.
    Your food chain must include the giraffe.   *1 mark*

(c) In the dry season thousands of wildebeest migrate long distances.
    Suggest one possible reason for this.   *1 mark*

    _____

    _____

(d) Look at the food chain below.

grass ⟶ zebra ⟶ lion

    (i)   Describe the energy transfers along the food chain.   *1 mark*

    _____

    _____

    _____

    (ii) What is the **original** source of energy for the plants and animals in the food chain?   *1 mark*

    _____

maximum 8 marks

4. The drawing shows one food chain in India.
   Cows eat grass. When a cow dies many vultures eat its dead body.

grass   cow   vulture

(a) Look at the picture of the vulture in the food chain.
    Give one way in which it is adapted to eating dead cows.   *1 mark*

_____

(b) In the space below draw a pyramid of numbers for the food chain.   *2 marks*

(c) When cows get ill, farmers give them a drug called diclofenac.
    Some of these cows later die.

   (i)   In the food chain above, vultures contain a higher concentration
         of diclofenac than cows. Explain why.   *2 marks*

   _____

   _____

   _____

   (ii) Many vultures die after eating meat from cows that have taken diclofenac.
         The vulture population has decreased. Use the food web below to suggest
         what will happen to the wild dog population.

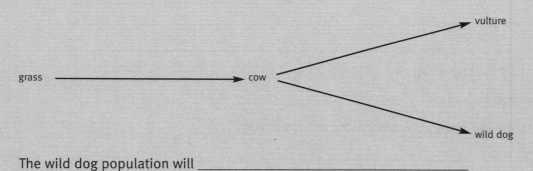

         The wild dog population will _____   *1 mark*

   (iii) Explain the reasoning for the answer you have given in part (c) (ii).   *1 mark*

   _____

   _____

   _____

maximum 7 marks

34

Particles

ACTIVITY A

✎ Draw a line to link two words on the oval.

Write a sentence on the line saying how the two words are connected.

✎ Repeat for as many pairs as you can.

solution

sugar   solvent

sand   solute

salt ——— *salt is soluble in water* ——— soluble

water   insoluble

dissolve

ACTIVITY B

✎ Write down the symbols for each of these elements. Use a periodic table to help you. You will end up with a sentence!

One word has been done for you.

- iodine, fluorine   --------------
- yttrium, oxygen, uranium   --------------
- potassium, nitrogen, oxygen, tungsten   --------------
- aluminium   --------------
- yttrium, oxygen, uranium   --------------
- calcium, nitrogen   --------------
- boron, oxygen, thorium   **B O Th** --------------
- potassium, iodine, sulphur, sulphur   --------------

ACTIVITY C

 From the words in the box, write the names of

- 6 elements
- 3 compounds
- 1 sedimentary rock
- 4 metals
- 2 non-metal elements
- 2 oxides
- 1 metamorphic rock

gold	sodium chloride	silver	sodium
chlorine	water	potassium	marble
sulphur dioxide	sandstone	iron oxide	silicon

ACTIVITY D

 Draw lines to match the diagrams to the descriptions.

diagrams

descriptions

P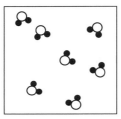

Q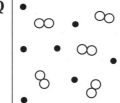

R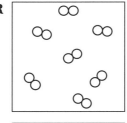

S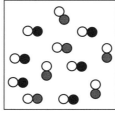

a mixture of two elements

a pure element

a pure compound

a mixture of two compounds

ACTIVITY E

Write 'P' next to each **physical change** and 'C' next to each **chemical change**.

Remember: in physical changes you **do not** make new substances; in chemical changes you **do** make new substances.

1. Dissolving sugar in tea ☐

2. Frying an egg ☐

3. Burning petrol in a car ☐

4. A limestone building being damaged by acid rain ☐

5. Using propanone to remove nail varnish ☐

6. Water getting into a small crack in a rock. The water freezes and expands. The rock breaks. ☐

7. Magma cooling to make granite crystals ☐

ACTIVITY F

Draw lines to match each observation to an explanation.

observations

A	You can smell someone's deodorant from the other side of the room.
B	The pressure inside a car tyre is high.
C	Sugar dissolves quicker in hot tea than in cold tea.
D	You can compress (squash) oxygen gas but you cannot compress oxygen liquid.
E	If liquid rock cools down quickly it makes small crystals. If liquid rock cools down slowly it makes big crystals.
F	If your gold ring is stuck on your finger you can sometimes get it off by running hot water over it.

explanations

1.	Hot liquid particles move around quicker than cold liquid particles. Hot solid particles vibrate faster than cold solid particles.
2.	The more slowly a liquid cools down, the more time there is for the particles to arrange themselves in a regular pattern.
3.	When you heat a solid the particles get more energy and move more. The particles get further apart.
4.	Gas particles spread out (diffuse) and mix with air particles.
5.	Gas particles move around fast and bump into the wall of the container they are in.
6.	The particles in a liquid are very close together. In a gas they are far apart.

ACTIVITY G

 Use the clues to fill in the grid.

The vertical word is a way of separating the different colours of ink in a pen.

1.   A gas . . . into a liquid.

2.   Sodium reacts with water to make sodium . . . and hydrogen.

3.   Liquid water . . . to make a solid at 0 °C.

4.   Mixtures contain more than . . . type of particle.

5.   . . . . . . separate particles of different sizes in living things.

6.   You can get pure water from seawater by . . .

7.   You can use copper for water pipes because copper does not react with . . .

8.   The temperature at which a liquid turns into a gas is called its . . . point.

9.   The . . . point of ice is 0 °C.

10. Use . . . to separate an insoluble solid from a liquid.

11. Something with a pH of less than 7 is an . . .

12. To get big copper sulphate crystals from copper sulphate solution
       you must let the water . . . slowly.

13. Magnesium reacts with steam to make magnesium oxide and . . .

14. Use . . . to extract a very reactive metal from its ore.

ACTIVITY H

When you are in love with someone, your brain makes two compounds every time you think of him or her. The compounds are:

dopamine $C_8H_{11}NO_2$ norepinephrine $C_8H_{11}NO_3$

1. How many different elements are there in one molecule of dopamine? ☐

2. How many carbon atoms are there in one molecule of norepinephrine? ☐

3. How many nitrogen atoms are there in one molecule of dopamine? ☐

4. Which compound has more oxygen atoms? _____

ACTIVITY I

Write word equations to represent each of these sentences.

Then write symbol equations for each reaction.

1. Alex held a piece of magnesium in a Bunsen burner flame. The magnesium joined with oxygen in the air to make magnesium oxide.

   magnesium + oxygen → magnesium oxide   _$2Mg + O_2 \rightarrow 2MgO$_

2. Iron reacts with sulphur to make iron sulphide.

   _____

3. Sam heated limestone (calcium carbonate). He made carbon dioxide and calcium oxide.

   _____

4. Peter mixed sodium hydroxide and hydrochloric acid. He made a neutral solution of sodium chloride and water.

   _____

5. Kezi burnt methane in oxygen. She made carbon dioxide gas and water vapour.

   _____

6. Joe added black copper oxide powder to nitric acid solution. He made copper nitrate solution and water.

   _____

7. Clare put a piece of potassium in a bowl of water. It whizzed around and made hydrogen gas. The other product of the reaction was alkaline potassium hydroxide solution.

   _____

8. Naomi mixed together aluminium powder and iron oxide powder. She heated the mixture. The aluminium displaced the iron to make aluminium oxide and iron.

   _____

Particles in solids, liquids and gases

Everything is made from tiny particles. Each particle in solid gold, liquid gold and gaseous gold is identical. But the particles in the solid, liquid and gas have different arrangements and behave differently.

	solid	liquid	gas
diagram of particle arrangement			
how are the particles arranged?	regular pattern	randomly	randomly
how close together are the particles?	very close	very close	very far apart
how strong are the forces between the particles?	very strong	strong	very weak
how do the particles move?	vibrate on the spot	move around between each other	move very fast in all directions

The particle model explains many things

You can compress gases but you cannot compress solids and liquids because
o The particles in solids and liquids touch each other. They cannot get any closer.
o The particles in gases are far apart. They get closer when you squash the gas.

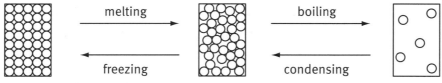

solid — not squashable   gas — squashable

Solids, liquids and gases expand when you heat them because the particles get more energy and move more. The particles get further apart and so the material becomes bigger. Each particle stays the same size.

Liquids and gases can diffuse. The particles spread out to fill the space they're in. This is **diffusion**.

Changes of state

solid →(melting) liquid →(boiling) gas
solid ←(freezing) liquid ←(condensing) gas

o When you heat a solid, the particles vibrate faster and faster. Eventually the particles start to move around, so they are no longer in a regular pattern. The solid has **melted** to make a liquid. Ice melts at 0 °C – this is its **melting point**. Pure elements and compounds have **fixed melting points**.
o When you heat a liquid, the particles get more energy and move faster and faster. The particles get further away from each other and the forces between the particles become weak. The liquid **boils** to make a gas. Water boils at 100 °C – this is its **boiling point**. Pure elements and compounds have **fixed boiling points**.

○ When a gas **condenses**, the particles move more slowly and get closer together to make a liquid.

○ When a liquid **freezes**, the particles arrange themselves in a regular pattern to make a solid. If a liquid cools quickly, the solid crystals are small. If the liquid cools slowly, the crystals are bigger because the particles have more time to arrange themselves in a regular pattern.

Particles in solution

If you add sugar to water, the sugar particles spread out and water particles surround them. The sugar **dissolves** to form a **solution**. Water is the **solvent** and sugar is the **solute**. Sugar is **soluble** in water. Sand does not dissolve in water; it is **insoluble**.

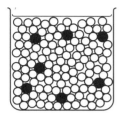

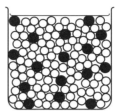

A **dilute** solution. There are very few sugar particles in 1 cm³ of solution.

A **concentrated** solution. There are more sugar particles in 1 cm³ of solution.

If you add 5 g of sugar to 100 g of water, the mass of the solution is 105 g. **Mass is conserved** because all the water and sugar particles are now in the solution. If you keep on adding sugar until no more will dissolve, you make a **saturated** solution.

Sugar dissolves quicker in hot water than in cold water. Also, the higher the temperature, the more sugar you can dissolve in 100 g of water. This is because hot water particles move fast and bump into the solid sugar often.

Particles in mixtures

Mixtures contain two or more types of particle. The different particles are not joined together – just mixed up. Mixtures do not have fixed melting and boiling points. It is usually easy to separate the components of a mixture.

○ Use **filtration** to separate an insoluble solid from a liquid.

○ Separate salt from water by **evaporation** if you want the salt, or by **distillation** if you want the water. This works for most solutions.

○ Separate the dyes in ink by **chromatography**. This works when you have more than one solute dissolved in a solvent.

Atoms, elements and compounds

○ Everything is made of tiny particles called **atoms**. There are about 100 types of atom.

○ An **element** is a substance that is made from only one type of atom. There are about 100 elements. All the elements are listed on the **periodic table**. Each element has its own **symbol** – for example, O for oxygen and K for potassium.

○ **Compounds** are made when atoms of different elements join together. The elements in each compound are in a fixed ratio. There are millions of different compounds. Each compound has a **formula**, for example CO_2 for carbon dioxide. In a carbon dioxide **molecule** one carbon atom is joined to two oxygen atoms. It is **difficult to separate** the atoms in a compound.

Chemical reactions

Chemical reactions – or chemical changes – **make new substances**. The atoms rearrange themselves, so the total mass of reactants is equal to the total mass of products – **mass is conserved**. All chemical reactions involve **energy changes**.

Burning

When a substance **reacts with oxygen** to make an oxide and give out heat energy, it is burning.

○ When **carbon** burns, one carbon atom reacts with one oxygen molecule to make one carbon dioxide molecule:

carbon + oxygen ⟶ carbon dioxide

$\underbrace{C\ +\ O_2}_{reactants}\ \longrightarrow\ \underset{product}{CO_2}$

○ **Hydrocarbons** burn in air to make carbon dioxide and water:

methane + oxygen ⟶ carbon dioxide + water

Carbon dioxide contributes to the **greenhouse effect**. Test for carbon dioxide by bubbling through limewater – the **limewater will go cloudy**.

Acid reactions

○ **Acids and carbonates** react to make a salt, carbon dioxide and water:

hydrochloric acid + calcium carbonate ⟶ calcium chloride + carbon dioxide + water

Acid rain is made when gases like sulphur dioxide dissolve in rainwater. The rain reacts with limestone (calcium carbonate), so damaging some buildings. It damages trees and makes lakes acidic – this kills fish.

○ **Acids and alkalis** react together in **neutralisation** reactions:

hydrochloric acid + sodium hydroxide ⟶ sodium chloride + water

HCl	+	NaOH	⟶	NaCl	+	H_2O
acidic		alkaline		neutral		neutral

○ **Acids react with metal oxides** to make a salt and water:

sulphuric acid + copper oxide ⟶ copper sulphate + water

H_2SO_4 +   CuO   ⟶ $CuSO_4$ + H_2O

Reactivity series of metals

The **reactivity series** lists metals in order of their reactivity. The metals at the top have more vigorous reactions than the metals at the bottom.

metal	symbol	how to extract the metal
potassium	K	electrolysis
sodium	Na	
magnesium	Mg	
zinc	Zn	reduce with carbon
iron	Fe	
copper	Cu	find the metal in
silver	Ag	the ground
gold	Au	

How metals react with oxygen, water and dilute acids

Metal	Reaction with oxygen	Reaction with water	Reaction with dilute acids
K	React with oxygen from the air (even when not heated). Make an **oxide**.	React vigorously with cold water to make **hydrogen** and a **metal hydroxide**.	React violently to make **hydrogen** and a **salt**.
Na			
Mg		React with steam to make **hydrogen** and a **metal oxide**.	React to make **hydrogen** and a **salt**.
Zn	React with oxygen when heated in air. Make an **oxide**.		
Fe			
Cu		Do not react with water or steam.	Do not react.
Ag	Do not react.		
Au			

Displacement reactions of metals

A **more reactive** metal displaces a **less reactive** metal from its oxide:

magnesium + iron oxide $\longrightarrow$ magnesium oxide + iron

$\quad$ 3Mg $\quad$ + $\quad$ Fe_2O_3 $\quad$ $\longrightarrow$ $\quad$ 3MgO $\quad$ + 2Fe

A **more reactive** metal displaces a **less reactive** metal from solutions:

iron + copper sulphate $\longrightarrow$ iron sulphate + copper

Fe $\quad$ + $\quad$ $CuSO_4$ $\quad$ $\longrightarrow$ $\quad$ $FeSO_4$ $\quad$ + $\quad$ Cu

Rocks – their properties and formation

Type of rock and diagram	How rocks of this type are made	Examples	Other information
Igneous	Magma (liquid rock from inside the Earth) cools and solidifies.	Granite Basalt	Made from interlocking crystals. Crystals are small if the magma cooled fast or big if the magma cooled slowly. Never contain fossils. Not porous.
Sedimentary	Rock fragments or the remains of animals and plants are deposited in layers. *or* Water evaporates from a lake that has minerals dissolved in it. Solid rock remains.	Limestone Sandstone	Small rough grains are cemented together. Often contain fossils. Often porous.
Metamorphic	Heat and high pressure changes other rocks.	Slate Marble	Grains are in lines or a random pattern. Occasionally contain fossils. Sometimes porous.

Particles

particles

- 3 states of matter
  - solid
  - liquid
    - melting
    - condensing
  - atoms
    - basic building blocks of matter
    - represented by symbols
      - e.g.
        - hydrogen = _ _ _
        - C =
- elements
  - all listed in the _ _ _ _ _ _ table
  - classified into _ _ _ _ — metals
    - metals → reactivity series
    - properties
      - conduct
  - different elements join together to make atoms of
    - represented by formulae
      - e.g. MgO =
      - water = _ _ _
- 3 types of rocks
  - metamorphic
  - sedimentary
  - igneous
- acids
  - pH 1 _ _ _
  - neutralised by
- can be rearranged
  - physical changes
    - e.g. → _ _ _ _ to reverse
  - chemical reactions
    - e.g. burning
      - carbon + oxygen →
    - involve energy change
    - total mass remains constant because _ _ _ _

1. The pH scale measures how acidic or alkaline a solution is.

pH scale

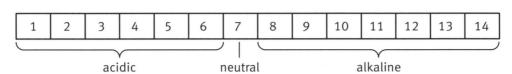

Different food crops grow best at different pHs:

food	soil pH at which the food grows best
cranberry	4–5
apple	5–6
sugar cane	6–8

(a) (i) From the table give the name of one food crop that can grow in slightly alkaline soil.

1 mark

_____

(ii) From the table give the name of the food crop that grows well in the most acidic soil.

1 mark

_____

(b) Edward wanted to find out the pH of the soil in his garden. He mixed universal indicator with soil and pure water. The pH of the soil was 7.

(i) What colour was the mixture of universal indicator, soil and pure water?
Tick the correct box.

1 mark

red ☐   orange ☐   green ☐   purple ☐

(ii) Edward wants to grow cranberries in his garden. What should he mix with the soil?
Use the table above to help you.
Tick the correct box.

1 mark

an acid ☐   universal indicator ☐   nothing ☐   an alkali ☐

maximum 4 marks

2. Tantalum is a metal. It is used to make artificial body joints like knees and hips.

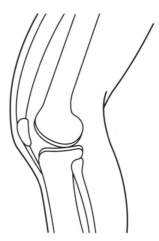

(a) This list shows some properties of tantalum.
   - It conducts heat.
   - It stores electrical charge.
   - It conducts electricity.
   - It does not react with water or acids.

   (i) Which **one** of the properties means that tantalum is a good metal to make artificial knee joints from?

   1 mark

   _____

   (ii) Which **two** of the properties in the list are properties of every metal?

   1 mark

   _____

   _____

(b) Tantalum has three physical states: solid, liquid and gas. In the boxes below draw the arrangement of particles in solid and liquid tantalum.

   2 marks

   Particles of solid tantalum　　　　　　　*Particles of liquid tantalum*

(c) The scale below shows the melting point and the boiling point of tantalum.

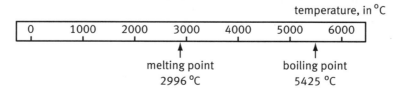

temperature, in °C

| 0 | 1000 | 2000 | 3000 | 4000 | 5000 | 6000 |

melting point
2996 °C

boiling point
5425 °C

   (i) At what temperature does liquid tantalum freeze?

   1 mark

   _____

   (ii) What is the physical state of tantalum at 2900 °C?

   1 mark

   _____

maximum 6 marks

3. Rizwana has four rings. Each ring is made from a different pure metal:
   copper, silver, gold and iron.

   (a) What is pure copper? Tick the correct box. *1 mark*

   a compound ☐   an element ☐   a mixture ☐   a solute ☐

   (b) Rizwana wrote down part of the reactivity series:

iron	most reactive
copper	
silver	
gold	least reactive

   (i) Rizwana wears all her rings every day for a month. The gold ring stays shiny for longest.
       Give one reason why. *1 mark*

       _____

       _____

   (ii) Rizwana drops all four rings in a beaker of hydrochloric acid.
        She sees bubbles coming from one ring.

   hydrochloric acid

        Which ring do the bubbles come from? _____ *1 mark*

        What gas is in the bubbles? _____ *1 mark*

   (c) Rizwana left the iron ring in a glass of water. After a week the iron had
       gone rusty. What **two** substances did the iron react with to make the rust? *1 mark*

       _____ and _____

   (d) Rizwana held her copper ring in a Bunsen burner flame.
       After five minutes the ring had gone black.
       Complete the word equation for this reaction. *2 marks*

       copper + _____ → _____

maximum 7 marks

4. Some buses use liquid propane gas for fuel.

   (a) The formula of propane is C_3H_8.

      (i) Name the two elements in propane.   *2 marks*

   _____ and _____

      (ii) What is the total number of atoms in one molecule of propane?   *1 mark*

   _____

   (b) Kathleen wanted to know what substances are made when propane burns.
   She found out the equation for the reaction from the internet.

   propane + oxygen ⟶ carbon dioxide + water

   She used the apparatus below to check the equation is correct.

ice cubes

vacuum pump

propane

liquid

limewater

      (i) Give the names of the two products of the reaction. Use the equation to help you.   *1 mark*

   _____ and _____

      (ii) What observation would show that carbon dioxide is made when
   propane burns? Use the diagram to help you.   *1 mark*

   _____

      (iii) Why did Kathleen put ice cubes at Y?   *1 mark*

   _____

   (c) The carbon dioxide that is made when fuels burn contributes to the greenhouse effect.
   Give two possible consequences of the greenhouse effect.   *2 marks*

   1._____

   2._____

   maximum 8 marks

ACTIVITY A

✎ Draw lines to match each diagram with its description.

diagrams

descriptions

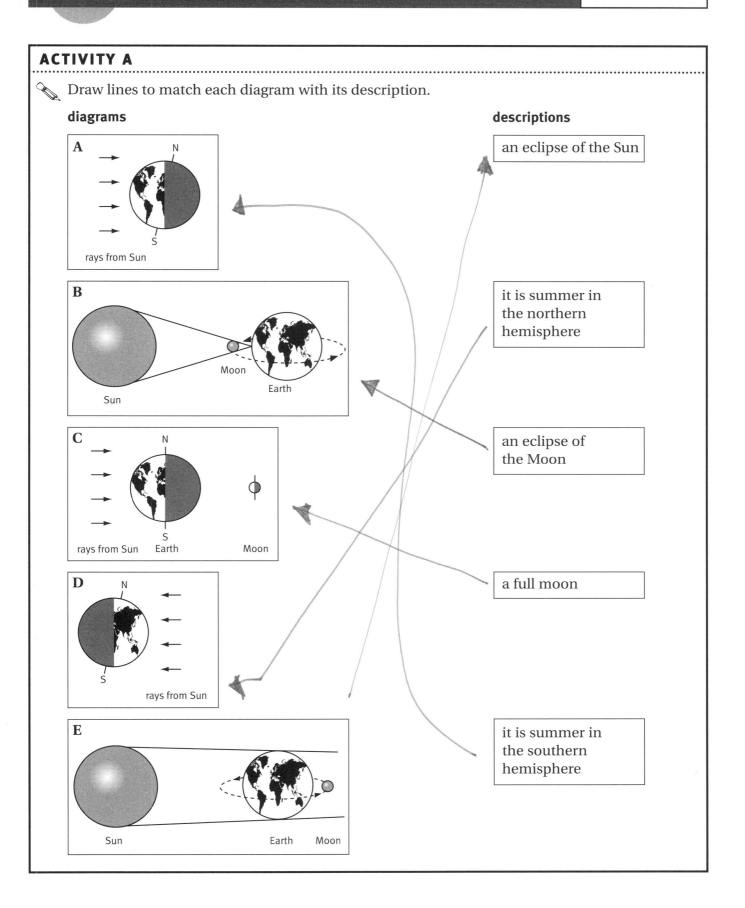

A
rays from Sun

B
Sun   Moon   Earth

C
rays from Sun   Earth   Moon

D
rays from Sun

E
Sun   Earth   Moon

an eclipse of the Sun

it is summer in the northern hemisphere

an eclipse of the Moon

a full moon

it is summer in the southern hemisphere

ACTIVITY B

 Make notes about gravity in the triangle:

- Write a title in the top section.
- Write the two or three most important points in the next section down.
- Write other, detailed, information in the lowest three levels.

ACTIVITY C

✏ In the box, write 'T' next to each true statement and 'F' next to each false statement.

1. A hamster has a smaller weight on Earth than on the Moon. ☐

2. If a motorbike moves at a steady speed the forces on it are balanced. ☐

3. The further a spacecraft is from Earth, the bigger the Earth's force of gravity on it. ☐

4. The friction between a car tyre and a smooth road surface is greater than the friction between the same car tyre and a rough road surface. ☐

5. Mass is measured in kilograms. ☐

6. A cat has the same mass on the Earth as on Jupiter. ☐

7. Weight is measured in kilograms. ☐

8. If a car is accelerating, the forces on it are balanced. ☐

9. Friction is a force that tries to stop two surfaces sliding over each other. ☐

10. You need a greater force to turn a long lever than you need to turn a short lever. ☐

11. The Sun is luminous. ☐

12. All metals are magnetic. ☐

13. You can reduce the friction between two surfaces with oil. ☐

14. All stars are light sources. ☐

15. Pressure measures how much force acts on a certain area. ☐

16. Electromagnets with iron cores are weaker than electromagnets without iron cores. ☐

17. The Moon orbits the Earth once every 24 hours. ☐

18. You can make an electromagnet stronger by increasing the current. ☐

ACTIVITY D

On each diagram, circle either **A** or **B** to show where the pressure is greater.

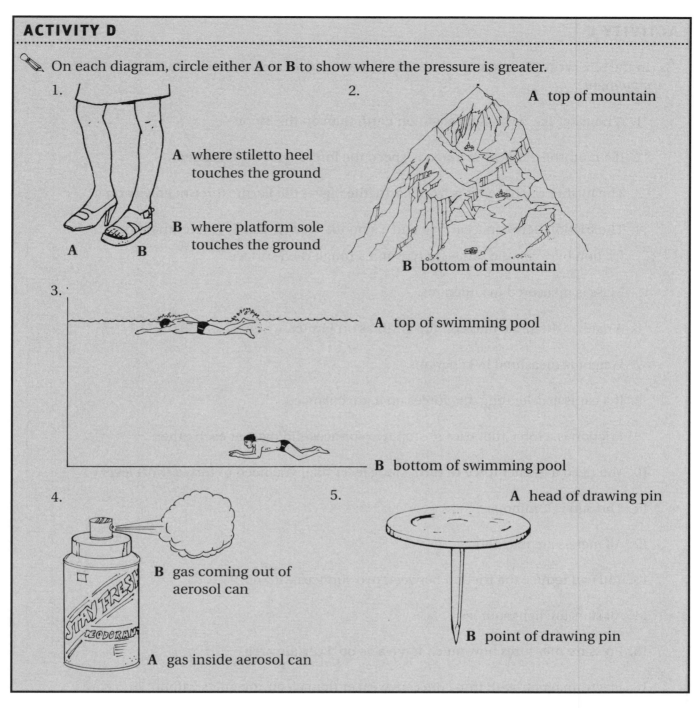

1.

A where stiletto heel touches the ground

B where platform sole touches the ground

A   **B**

2.

A top of mountain

B bottom of mountain

3.

A top of swimming pool

B bottom of swimming pool

4.

B gas coming out of aerosol can

A gas inside aerosol can

5.

A head of drawing pin

B point of drawing pin

ACTIVITY E

Write down **two** ways that Victoria and David could balance the seesaw.

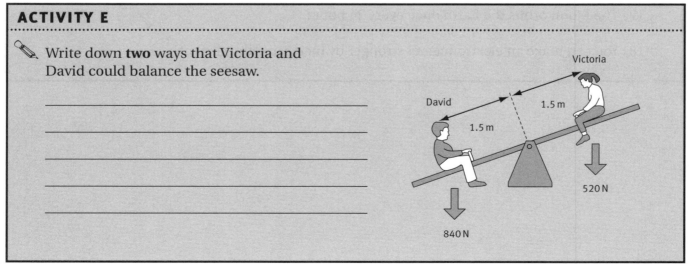

David
1.5 m
840 N

Victoria
1.5 m
520 N

_____

_____

_____

_____

ACTIVITY F

 Circle the correct answer to each calculation.

1. An elephant charges 50 metres in 5 seconds. Its average speed is

   A 250 m/s   **B** 25 m/s

   C 0.1 m/s   **D** 10 m/s

2. A hippopotamus has a mass of 1400 kg. On Earth, 1 kilogram is equivalent to 10 newtons. The weight of the hippopotamus on Earth is

   A 14 000 N   **B** 140 N

   C 1410 N   **D** 1390 N

3. A camel weighs 7000 N. The total area under its feet is 3000 cm^2. The pressure under the camel's feet is

   A 0.43 N/cm^2 **B** 2.3 N/cm^2

   C 230 N/cm^2 **D** 430 N/cm^2

4. A chimpanzee weighs 400 N. She is sitting 2 m from the pivot of a seesaw. The turning moment of the chimpanzee is

   A 800 N m   **B** 200 N m

   C 80 N m   **D** 20 N m

5. A lion runs 1000 m in 50 s. Its speed is

   A 20 m/s   **B** 50 000 m/s

   C 200 m/s   **D** 100 m/s

6. The length of a human's forearm is 0.3 m. He bends his arm at the elbow and picks up a weight of 20 N. The turning moment of the load is

   A 6 N m   **B** 60 N m

   C 67 N m   **D** 667 N m

7. A gold ring has a mass of 2 g. Its volume is 0.1 cm^3. The density of gold is

   A 0.2 g/cm^3 **B** 2 g/cm^3

   C 20 g/cm^3 **D** 200 g/cm^3

Forces are **pushes** or **pulls**. Every force has a **size** and acts in a certain **direction**. Forces act in **pairs**.

Balanced forces

If forces are **balanced**, there is no change in movement. Forces are balanced on **stationary** objects (things that are not moving), **floating** objects, and objects that are **moving at a constant speed.**

Floating objects

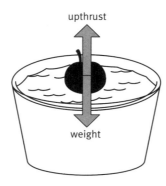

upthrust

weight

Upthrust = weight

To find out if something floats, you need to know its density.

density = mass ÷ volume

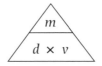

The apple's mass is 150 g and its volume is 200 cm^3.

density = 150 g ÷ 200 cm^3 = 0.75 g/cm^3

The density of the apple (0.75 g/cm^3) is less than the density of water (1 g/cm^3) so the apple floats.

Objects moving at a constant speed

Forward force = backward force or *thrust = drag*

Use this formula to calculate speed:

speed = distance ÷ time

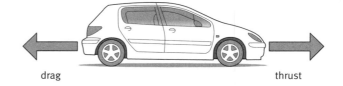

drag   thrust

Unbalanced forces

Two forces are **unbalanced** if the force in one direction is more than the force in another direction. Unbalanced forces can change an object's **shape**, **direction** and **speed**.

Changing speed

A car is travelling at a steady speed, so the forces on it are balanced. The driver puts her foot on the accelerator. The **thrust** force increases and becomes larger than the **drag**. Now the forces are **unbalanced**. The car gets faster (accelerates).

Levers and moments

Scissors and arms are both levers. They are simple machines that use pivots to make tasks easier.

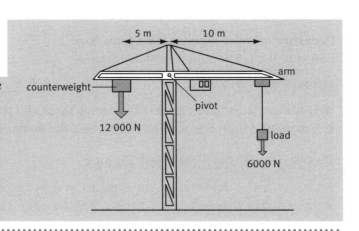

Forces make things turn round pivots. A **moment** is the turning effect of a force.

The longer the lever, the greater the turning force (and the easier the job!).

moment = force × perpendicular distance from the pivot

To balance a crane, the anticlockwise moment must be equal to the clockwise moment.

Friction

Friction between solid surfaces

Friction is a force that that tries to stop a surface moving over another surface. Friction is **useful** for **brakes**, to make your shoes **grip** the floor and to keep your shoelaces tied.

Sometimes friction is **not useful**. It makes things slow down. Also, it makes moving parts in machines (like cars) heat up. You can reduce friction by putting a **lubricant** (like oil) between the moving parts.

Friction in liquids and gases

Air resistance is a frictional force that pushes against – and slows down – objects that move through the air. For example, air resistance is the biggest frictional force pushing against a car on a motorway.

Water resistance is a frictional force that pushes against objects moving through water.

Air and water resistance depend on

o **Speed** – the faster a car travels, the greater the air resistance. More air particles oppose the movement of the car.

o **Shape** – the more streamlined a boat, the smaller the water resistance. Fewer water particles oppose the movement of a streamlined shape.

The **forces on a falling object** change as the object goes down:

o At first **gravity** is the only force on the man. He accelerates.

o As he falls faster, **air resistance** increases.

o When the parachute opens, **air resistance** increases more. The man falls more slowly.

o Soon, the forces of **gravity** and **air resistance** are the same size. The man falls at a steady speed until he hits the ground.

Pressure

Pressure is how concentrated a force is, or how much force acts on a certain area.

pressure = force ÷ area

- You want a low pressure on skis, snowboards and the head of a drawing pin.
- You want a high pressure on a knife and the point of a drawing pin.

Pressure in liquids and gases

When you swim underwater, the pressure you feel depends on the weight of water above you. The deeper you are, the greater the weight of water above you and the higher the pressure.

The air in car tyres is at a higher pressure than the air around us. The pressure is high in tyres because air particles hit the inside of the tyre walls very frequently.

- Fire hoses use high-pressure water jets so that water comes out quickly.
- Hydraulic jacks use liquids under pressure. The high pressure is transmitted to all parts of the liquid.

Magnets

Magnets only attract **magnetic materials**. These are iron, steel, cobalt, nickel and iron oxide.

Unlike poles (north and south) of two magnets attract each other. Like poles (north and north or south and south) of two magnets repel each other. You must use repulsion to test whether something is a magnet or not.

You can **make a permanent magnet** by stroking a magnetic material with a magnet.

You can **make an electromagnet** by coiling a wire round an iron core, and passing an electric current through the wire. The electromagnet gets stronger if you
- add more coils
- increase the current
- make the core into a horseshoe shape

Magnetic forces can act through non-magnetic materials, like paper. They cannot act through magnetic materials – this is called **magnetic shielding**.

- You can use permanent magnets on noticeboards and to close cupboard doors.
- Electromagnets are used in car scrapyards, doorbells and speakers.

The area of force around a magnet is called a **magnetic field**. There is a magnetic field around the Earth. This is why the magnet in a compass needle always points north.

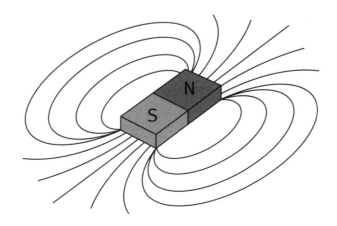

The magnetic field round a bar magnet

Mass, weight, gravity and our Solar System

o **Mass** is the amount of matter in an object. It is measured in **kilograms** (kg).

o **Weight** is a force. It is measured in **newtons** (N).

o **Gravity** is a force of attraction between objects. If you drop a ball anywhere on Earth it always falls towards the centre of the Earth. The size of a gravitational force depends on the **masses** of the objects and the **distance** between them.

Grace has a mass of 50 kg. This mass does not change, wherever she is. Her weight on Earth is 500 N. But her weight on Jupiter is 2700 N. Jupiter has a bigger mass than Earth. So the force of gravity on Grace when she is on Jupiter is bigger than it is on Earth. So Grace weighs more on Jupiter.

The Sun has an enormous mass. The Sun's gravitational force keeps **planets orbiting** round it. The Earth's gravitational force keeps **satellites orbiting** the Earth. The Moon is a natural satellite. We use artificial satellites to forecast weather, transmit TV signals and to study the Solar System.

The Sun and other stars are **luminous** – they give out light. Planets and satellites are **non-luminous**. We can only see them because they reflect light from the Sun.

The Earth takes a **day** to spin once on its axis. The Moon takes a **month** to orbit the Earth. The Earth takes a **year** to orbit the Sun.

When the Earth is directly between the Sun and the Moon, there is an **eclipse of the Moon**. When the Moon is directly between the Sun and the Earth, there is an **eclipse of the Sun**.

The shape of the Moon looks different every night of the month. This pattern is called the **phases of the moon**.

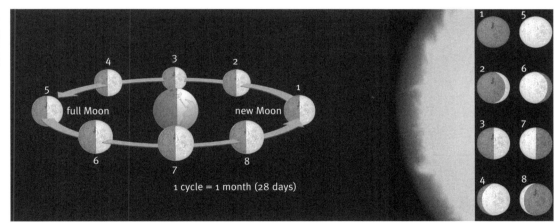

We have seasons because the Earth is **tilted**. When the northern hemisphere is tilted towards the Sun we have long days and short nights in Britain. It is summer.

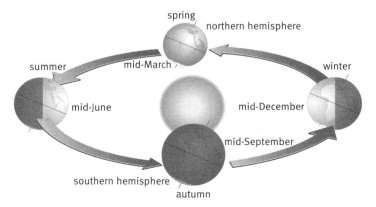

CONCEPT MAP

Forces

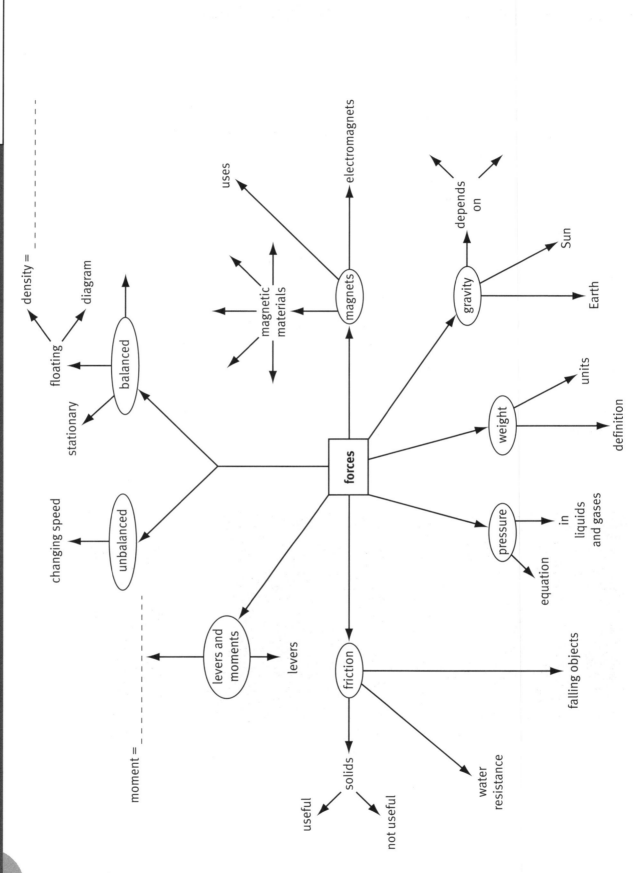

forces

balanced
- stationary
- floating
  - density =
  - diagram

unbalanced
- changing speed

magnetic materials

magnets
- uses
- electromagnets

gravity
- depends on
- Sun
- Earth

levers and moments
- moment =
- levers

friction
- solids
  - useful
  - not useful
- water resistance
- falling objects

pressure
- equation
- in liquids and gases

weight
- units
- definition

1. The picture shows a baby in an inflatable raft. A person is pushing her across a swimming pool. The arrows show the forces on the raft.

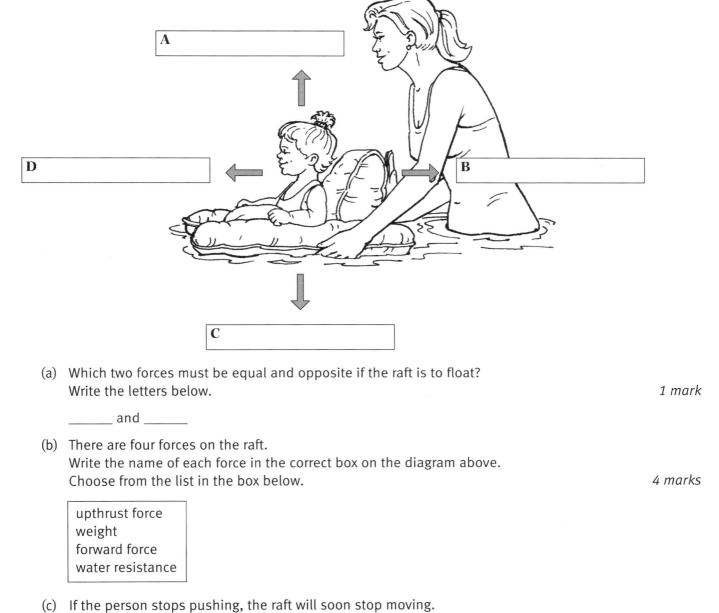

A

D

B

C

(a) Which two forces must be equal and opposite if the raft is to float?
Write the letters below.

1 mark

_____ and _____

(b) There are four forces on the raft.
Write the name of each force in the correct box on the diagram above.
Choose from the list in the box below.

4 marks

> upthrust force
> weight
> forward force
> water resistance

(c) If the person stops pushing, the raft will soon stop moving.
Why will the raft stop moving?
Tick the correct box.

1 mark

water resistance slows it down ☐

water resistance gets less ☐

the upthrust decreases ☐

the upthrust increases ☐

maximum 6 marks

2. Samira has a magnet.

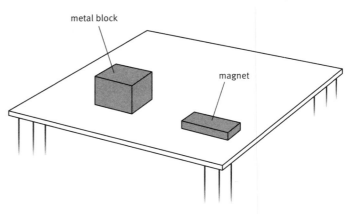

metal block

magnet

(a) Samira wants to use her magnet to make a metal block move along the surface of a table.

    (i) Suggest two metals the block could be made from.   *2 marks*

_____ and _____

    (ii) Give the name of the force that tries to stop the metal block sliding over the table.   *1 mark*

_____

    (iii) Samira wants to stop the magnet attracting the metal block. She puts a thin sheet between the magnet and the metal block. What could the thin sheet be made of? Tick the correct box.   *1 mark*

wood ☐   plastic ☐

glass ☐   steel ☐

(b) (i) Draw a diagram to show how Samira could use her magnet to point to the Earth's magnetic north pole.   *1 mark*

    (ii) Give **one other** use for the magnet.   *1 mark*

_____

(c) Draw lines of force round the magnet below to show the shape of its magnetic field.   *2 marks*

maximum 8 marks

3. In 2003, scientists discovered the most faraway object to orbit the Sun. This object is called Sedna.

The diagram shows the distance of Sedna from the Sun compared to two planets of our Solar System, Pluto and Earth.

distance from the Sun

Sun	Earth	Pluto	Sedna
	0.15 billion kilometres	5.9 billion kilometres	17 billion kilometres

(a) What force keeps Sedna in orbit around the Sun?

1 mark

_____

(b) The table gives information about five objects that orbit the Sun.

object	time to orbit the Sun, in Earth years	average temperature, in °C	time to rotate on axis, in Earth days
Saturn	29	−190	0.4
Uranus	84	−210	0.7
Neptune	165	−220	0.7
Pluto	248	−240	6.4
Sedna	10 500	−240	20

(i) Which object in the table rotates on its axis most slowly?

1 mark

_____

(ii) Give **one** reason why it takes Sedna more time to orbit the Sun than Pluto. Use the diagram above.

1 mark

_____

_____

(iii) Give **one** reason why Pluto and Sedna are colder than the other objects in the table. Use the diagram above.

1 mark

_____

_____

(c) Sedna is not a light source but scientists have seen it through telescopes. Explain why scientists can see Sedna even though it is not a light source.

1 mark

_____

_____

maximum 5 marks

4. (a) An athlete runs 100 metres in 10.0 seconds. Calculate his average speed. Give the unit.

2 marks

_____

_____

(b) The athlete buys some new running clothes so he is more streamlined. He now runs 100 metres in 9.9 seconds.

(i) One of the forces on the athlete is reduced when he is more streamlined. Give the name of this force.

1 mark

_____

(ii) Use the idea of **particles** to explain **why** this force is less when the athlete is more streamlined.

2 marks

_____

_____

(c) The athlete runs in a 100 metre race.
A graph of **distance** against **time** for the athlete is shown below.

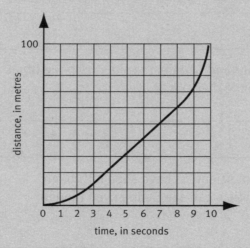

(i) Describe the motion of the athlete between 4 seconds and 8 seconds.

1 mark

_____

(ii) Describe the motion of the athlete between 9 seconds and 10 seconds.

1 mark

_____

maximum 7 marks

ACTIVITY A

 Circle the mistake in each circuit.

Under each circuit draw another circuit diagram with the same components but no mistakes.

1.

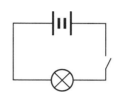

2.

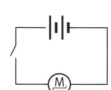

3.

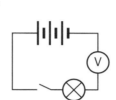

4.

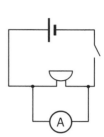

ACTIVITY B

 Fill in the gaps using the words from the box.

chemical	volts	components	energy	kinetic
smaller	transformed	potential	sound	

A car has many electrical _____, for example headlights

and a radio. When the engine is not running, the _____

source for the car's electrical circuits is the battery. The battery stores

_____ energy. In the car's circuits, chemical energy is

_____ into electrical energy. The battery 'pushes' electric

charges round the circuits. This push is called the _____

difference. It is measured in _____ .

The headlights transform electrical energy to light energy. The radio transforms

electrical energy to _____ energy. The starting motor

transforms electrical energy to _____ energy.

A bigger current flows through the starting motor than flows through the horn.

So the starting motor has the _____ resistance.

ACTIVITY C

✎ Fill the gaps in the boxes to show how electricity companies generate electricity.

Add arrows and labels to the diagram to show where energy is wasted.

Words to use:
electricity   steam   turbine   wind   coal   biofuel   generator   tides   oil   gas

Burn a fossil fuel, for example _____ , _____ or _____ .

Burn a _____ like methane, which can be made in sewage treatment works.

Use a windmill to 'collect' energy from the _____ or a tidal barrage to 'collect' energy from _____ .

Heat up water to make _____ .

Make the _____ turn.

Make the _____ turn (this is a big coil of wire in a magnetic field).

You have generated _____ !

ACTIVITY D

✎ Fill in the target board by answering the question in each part of the circle.

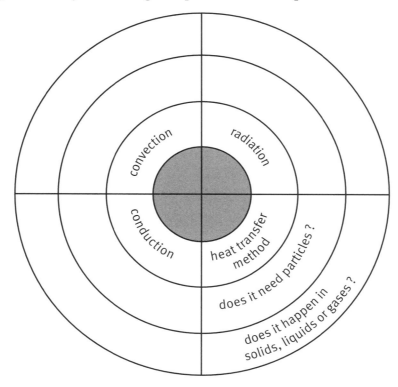

ACTIVITY E

✎ Write the letter of one example next to each temperature on the Celsius scale.

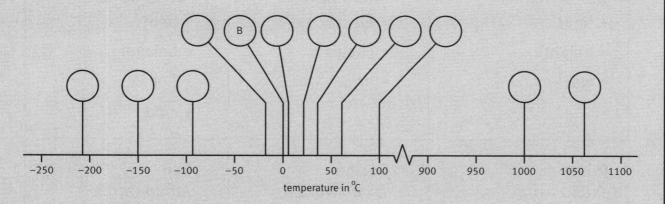

temperature in °C

Examples

A boiling point of water

B melting point of ice

C room temperature

D human body temperature

E fridge temperature

F freezer temperature

G temperature of coldest day recorded anywhere on Earth

H temperature of warmest day recorded anywhere on Earth

I melting point of gold

J temperature at which nitrogen gas condenses to a liquid

K temperature of a candle flame

L average temperature on the surface of Jupiter

ACTIVITY F

Do this activity with a friend.

✎ Define the word at the top of the card. Do not use the 'taboo' words.

Get your friend to guess the word you are defining.

Fuel	**Solar cells**	**Convection**
Taboo words	*Taboo words*	*Taboo words*
● energy	● Sun	● particles
● burn	● light	● heat
● coal	● electricity	● liquid
● petrol	● renewable	● gas
Refraction	**Sound waves**	**Complete circuit**
Taboo words	*Taboo words*	*Taboo words*
● light	● vibrations	● electricity
● change direction	● hear	● current
● glass	● frequency	● flow
Amplitude	**Current**	**Temperature**
Taboo words	*Taboo words*	*Taboo words*
● loud	● electricity	● heat
● height	● circuit	● Celsius
● wave	● flow	● hot
		● cold
Prism	**Decibel**	**Sun**
Taboo words	*Taboo words*	*Taboo words*
● light	● loudness	● energy source
● dispersion	● volume	● star
● spectrum	● unit	● hot
● glass		

ACTIVITY G

 Colour the diagrams to show what you would see.

When you shine green light at a green filter, you see green light.
The green light is **transmitted**.

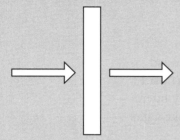

When you shine red light at a green filter, you see no light.
The red light is **absorbed**.

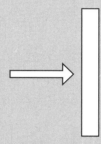

When you shine white light at a blue filter, you see blue light.
The blue light is **transmitted**. The other colours are **absorbed**.

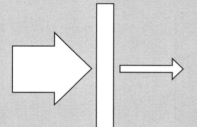

When you colour this diagram show that white light is made of the seven colours of the spectrum – red, orange, yellow, green, blue, indigo and violet.

ACTIVITY H

 Cross out the bold words that are **not** correct.

1. Strawberries look red in red light because they reflect **red/green/blue** light.

2. Strawberries look **red/green/black** in white light because they reflect **red/green/blue** light and absorb all the other colours.

3. Strawberries look **red/green/black** in blue light because they **absorb/reflect** blue light. There is no red light to **absorb/reflect**.

4. Peas look **red/green/black** in white light because they **reflect/absorb** green light and **reflect/absorb** the other colours.

5. Peas look **red/green/black** in red light because they **reflect/absorb** red light and there is no **green/black/red** light to reflect.

Energy resources

The Sun is the source of most of the Earth's energy resources.

Fossil fuels

Coal, oil and gas are **fossil fuels**. They were made millions of years ago from dead plants and animals. They store **chemical energy** which is transferred to **heat and light energy** when they burn. Fossil fuels make carbon dioxide gas when they burn. This gas contributes to the **greenhouse effect**. Burning coal and oil also make a gas that contributes to **acid rain**.

We use **coal** for heating and generating electricity, **gas** for cooking, heating and generating electricity and **oil** to make petrol and diesel for cars and lorries.

Fossil fuels are **non-renewable** because they take so long to make. Eventually, our reserves of these fuels will run out. We need to **conserve** coal, oil and gas.

You can **conserve fossil fuels**
o at home by installing roof insulation, double glazing and low-energy light bulbs
o by walking, cycling or going by bus instead of travelling by car
o by turning off lights, computers and televisions

Generating electricity

Many power stations burn fossil fuels to generate electricity:

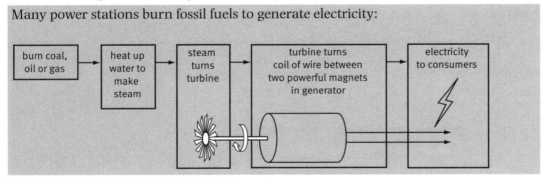

We can conserve fossil fuels by generating electricity from **renewable** energy resources. Renewable resources are replaced all the time, so they will not run out.

Renewable energy resources generate electricity in different ways:
o **Wind**, **hydroelectric** (water) and **tidal** power turn turbines directly.
o **Geothermal** power stations use heat energy from below the Earth's surface to make steam to turn turbines.
o **Solar cells** use light energy from the Sun to make an electric current – this system does not use turbines.

Renewable energy resources also provide **heating**. Active **solar panels** use heat energy from the Sun to heat up water. Sewage treatment works and rubbish dumps make **methane** gas that we burn to release heat energy. Methane is an example of a **biofuel**.

Energy transfer

Energy makes things happen. To be useful, energy must be **transferred** from one place to another or **transformed** into a different sort of energy. When energy is transferred or transformed, the **total** amount of energy is **constant**. Energy has been **conserved**.

Many energy transfers happen when you eat a banana and then go swimming. The Sun is the energy **source**. **Light** energy from the Sun is transferred to **chemical** energy in the banana plant through photosynthesis. Chemical energy from the banana is **transferred** to your body. While you swim, chemical energy in your body is **transformed** into different types of energy: **kinetic** (movement), **heat** and **sound**.

These energy transfers happen during hydroelectric power generation:

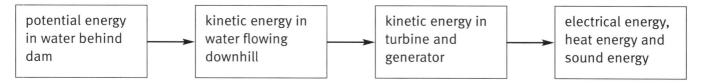

| potential energy in water behind dam | → | kinetic energy in water flowing downhill | → | kinetic energy in turbine and generator | → | electrical energy, heat energy and sound energy |

The electrical energy is **useful**, but the sound and heat energy are **dissipated** or **wasted**. It is more **efficient** to generate electricity in a hydroelectric power station than in a coal-fired power station – the hydroelectric power station makes less waste heat energy.

Heating and cooling

Temperature measures how hot things are. Its units are degrees Celsius (°C).

Heat (thermal) energy flows from one thing to another when there is a **temperature difference** – the energy always goes from the hotter thing to the cooler thing. When a cup of coffee cools, heat energy transfers from the coffee to the surroundings. Heat energy is measured in joules (J).

Heat energy is transferred by **conduction**, **convection** and **radiation**.

○ **Metals** are good **thermal conductors**. In **conduction** heat energy transfers from particle to particle. A hot particle vibrates faster than its neighbours – it has more kinetic energy. The particle transfers this energy to its neighbours, and eventually the whole piece of metal gets hotter.

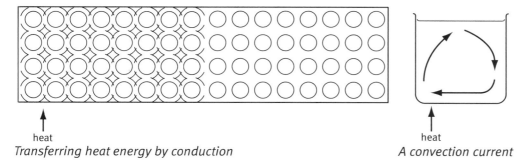

heat
Transferring heat energy by conduction

heat
A convection current

○ **Liquids** and **gases** transfer heat mainly by **convection**. If you heat one side of the bottom of a beaker of water, the water gets warmer. It is less dense than the water above it, so it rises to the top. Cold water falls and takes its place. This is called a **convection current**. Particles transfer the thermal energy from one place to another.

○ Hot things give out **infrared radiation**. Radiation can transfer heat energy through a **vacuum** – it does not need moving particles.

69

Electricity

Energy transfer in electric circuits

Electric circuits need a source of energy. **Cells** are the energy source in mobile phones. Cells store **chemical energy**. This chemical energy is transformed into **electrical energy** in the circuit. Cells push electric charges round the circuit. This push is called the **potential difference**. The size of the push is measured in **volts** using a **voltmeter**.

Electric current flows round a circuit. It **carries energy** from the cell to components in the circuit. The components transform electrical energy into other forms. Motors transform electrical energy to kinetic energy and lamps transform electrical energy to light energy.

Energy is **conserved** in electric circuits. The amount of energy transferred from the cell is the same as the total amount of energy that is transformed by the components into light energy, kinetic energy and so on.

You can use an **ammeter** to measure the flow of current in a circuit. The unit for current is **amps**. In a **series circuit** the current is the same everywhere in the circuit. In a **parallel circuit** the current divides along the different branches. Christmas tree lights are sometimes wired in series – if one light goes out, they all do. Car headlights are wired in parallel – if one light goes out, the other still works.

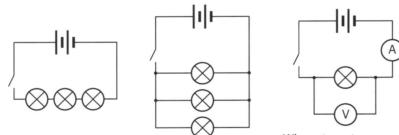

A series circuit   *A parallel circuit*   *Where to put an ammeter and a voltmeter to find the current and voltage at a lamp*

All components resist the flow of current in a circuit. The **resistance** of a circuit that has two lamps is greater than the resistance of a circuit that has just one of the lamps. The current is smaller in circuits with higher resistance.

Mains electricity

At home electricity flows in electrical circuits from 'the mains' to appliances like televisions and electrical heaters. Some appliances transform energy more quickly than others – a heater transfers 2000 joules every second; its power rating is 2000 watts. The power rating of a television is 120 watts. It is cheaper to watch television for an hour than to use an electric heater for an hour.

High-voltage electric circuits are dangerous because humans are good conductors of electricity. Nerves carry electrical signals around your body. If you touch a high-voltage wire a massive current might travel along the nerves that control your heart.

Light

Light transfers energy when it travels from a **source**. Light travels in straight lines. It travels very fast – at 300 000 000 m/s. Light can travel through empty space – it does not need a **medium**.

We can see **luminous** objects (like the Sun or a light bulb) because light rays travel from them into our eyes. We see **non-luminous** objects because light from a light source reflects from them and goes into our eyes.

Mirrors reflect light rays. The **angle of incidence** is equal to the **angle of reflection**. The image in a plane (flat) mirror is **laterally inverted** (back to front).

How we see a non-luminous object

Light rays change direction when they go from one medium to another at an angle. This is **refraction**. When light goes from one medium to a denser medium, the **angle of refraction** is less than the **angle of incidence**.

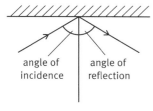

angle of
incidence

angle of
reflection

Reflection

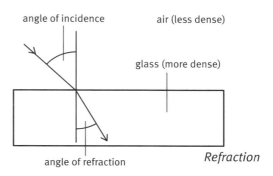

angle of incidence

air (less dense)

glass (more dense)

angle of refraction

Refraction

White light is made from a mixture of colours. When you shine white light through a prism the light **disperses** (splits up) and you see **a spectrum**.

If you shine white light at a blue filter, only blue light is **transmitted**. All the other colours are **absorbed**. If you shine red light at a blue filter, you see nothing. The blue filter transmits blue light only, so it absorbs all the red light.

A red car looks red in white light. This is because it **reflects** red light and **absorbs** all the other colours. In green light the red car looks black because it absorbs the green light and there is no red light to reflect.

Sound

When sound travels it transfers energy. Sound travels from a **source** by **vibration** – the vibrations are called **sound waves**. Sound must travel through a **medium** because the vibrations need to pass from one particle to another. The speed of sound in air is 330 m/s. Sound travels faster in solids because the particles are closer together.

Sound waves have **amplitude** and **frequency**. Sounds with a big amplitude are loud. Loudness is measured in **decibels** (dB). Sounds with a high frequency are high-pitched. Frequency is measure in **hertz** (Hz).

Low frequency (low-pitched)

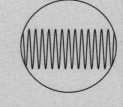

High frequency (high-pitched)

Small amplitude (quiet)

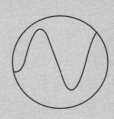

Large amplitude (loud)

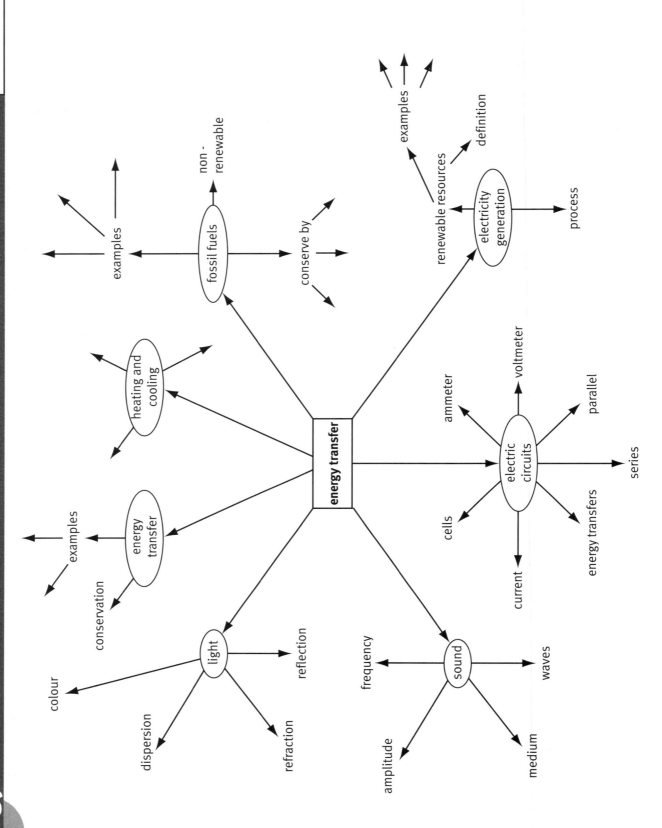

energy transfer

- fossil fuels
  - examples
  - non-renewable
  - conserve by
- heating and cooling
- energy transfer
  - examples
  - conservation
- renewable resources
  - examples
  - electricity generation
    - definition
    - process
- electric circuits
  - ammeter
  - voltmeter
  - parallel
  - series
  - energy transfers
  - cells
  - current
- light
  - reflection
  - colour
  - dispersion
  - refraction
- sound
  - frequency
  - waves
  - amplitude
  - medium

1. Alison has a new car. The diagram below shows how the headlights are connected to the battery of the car.

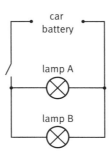

(a) (i) Give the name of this type of circuit.   *1 mark*

_____

(ii) Lamp A blows. What will happen to lamp B?   *1 mark*

_____

(b) (i) What is the energy source for the circuit above?   *1 mark*

_____

(ii) Fill the gaps below to show the energy transfers that take place
when the lamps are on.   *3 marks*

_____ energy in the circuit is transformed into

_____ and _____ energy in the lamp.

(c) Alison adds four ammeters to the circuit. She reads the current on each ammeter.

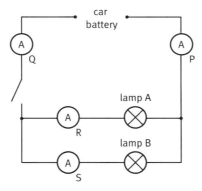

Which of the statements below are correct? Tick **two** boxes.   *2 marks*

The current at P is the same as the current at R.   ☐

The current at P is the same as the current at Q.   ☐

The current at Q is bigger than the current at S.   ☐

The current at S is bigger than the current at P.   ☐

maximum 8 marks

2. (a) Mary shines a ray of light at a glass block.

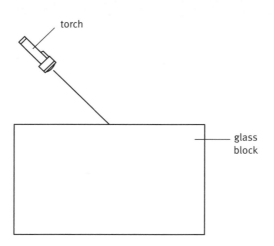

The ray of light changes direction when it reaches the glass block.

(i) Use a ruler to draw the ray of light going through the glass block. *2 marks*

(ii) Add arrows to the rays to show the direction of the light. *1 mark*

(b) Mary also shines light rays at a mirror and at a prism.
Draw a straight line from the name of the apparatus to the word
that describes what happens to the light. *3 marks*

name of apparatus

**word that describes
what happens to the light**

prism		reflection

glass block		refraction

mirror		dispersion

maximum 6 marks

3. The people of a city want to generate their own electricity. They must decide which type of power station to build. Their three options are listed below.

- A coal-fired power station
- Wind turbines
- A power station that generates electricity from methane gas.

    The methane will come from a local rubbish tip.

(a) Each method of generating electricity has benefits and problems. Draw straight lines from the method of generating electricity to a benefit of this method and to a problem of this method. *3 marks*

benefit	**method**	**problem**
can generate electricity all the time	coal-fired power station	cannot generate electricity all the time
makes good use of waste materials	wind turbines	produces a gas that makes acid rain
does not make gases that pollute the atmosphere	methane gas power station at rubbish tip	relies on people making enough rubbish

(b) Give the names of **two** other renewable energy resources that can generate electricity. *2 marks*

_____ and _____

(c) Fill the gaps to show the energy transfers that take place in a coal-fired power station. *3 marks*

Energy from sunlight is transformed to _____

energy in coal. The coal burns to release _____

energy, which is transferred to water. Then steam makes turbines turn.

The turbines have _____ energy. This is

transformed to electrical energy.

maximum 8 marks

75

4. Aidan did an experiment to find out the highest frequency sounds that different people and animals can hear. His results are in the table below.

person or animal	age, in years	highest frequency the person or animal can hear, in hertz
Finan	11	28 000
David	42	20 000
Woody the dog	6	39 000

(a) (i) Aidan blew a whistle. The whistle made vibrations with a frequency of 25 000 hertz. Who could hear the whistle? Tick the correct box.

1 mark

Finan and David ☐   Woody only ☐

Finan and Woody ☐   Finan only ☐

(ii) The statements below describe how David hears the whistle.

A The eardrum passes on vibrations to bones in the middle ear.	**B** The bones pass the vibrations to the cochlea.	**C** The whistle makes air particles vibrate.
D The cochlea transforms vibrations into electrical signals.	**E** Vibrating air particles make the eardrum vibrate.	**F** The electrical signals travel along nerve cells to the brain.

In the boxes below write the letters in the correct order to describe how David hears the whistle. One has been done for you.

5 marks

[C] ☐ ☐ ☐ ☐ ☐

(b) The diagrams below show the patterns made by four sound waves on an oscilloscope screen.

W   X   Y   Z

Write the letter of

4 marks

(i) the loudest sound ☐

(ii) the sound with the highest pitch ☐

(iii) the wave with the smallest amplitude ☐

(iv) the wave with the highest frequency ☐

maximum 10 marks

ACTIVITY A

Only some of these questions are suitable for scientific enquiry.

 Highlight or tick the ones which are.

Which type of indigestion tablet neutralises most acid?

Which type of deodorant smells best?

Does deodorant cause breast cancer?

At the bottom of which British swimming pool is the pressure highest?

Which make of mobile phone is best?

Does food go mouldy quicker in a cold room or a hot room?

ACTIVITY B

Here are the results of some scientific enquiries.

 Write down the questions the students were investigating.

length of slug, in cm	2.1	3.9	5.0	8.2	9.3
mass of slug, in grams	4.0	8.3	9.8	17.4	18.2

Question: _____

_____

height we dropped the football from, in cm	50	70	100	150	170
height of the first bounce, in cm	44	61	81	133	126

Question: _____

_____

pH of rainwater	5.0	5.4	6.0	6.7	7.0
height of new plant after two weeks, in cm	4.8	5.7	5.8	5.7	5.4

Question: _____

_____

ACTIVITY C

Kathleen is investigating the question 'how does the temperature of water affect the speed that sugar dissolves in it?'.

✎ Highlight or circle the equipment she needs.

| measuring cylinder | newtonmeter | forehead thermometer |

| stopwatch | stirring rod | beaker |

| ruler | temperature probe attached to computer |

| kettle | light gates attached to computer |

| balance | Universal indicator | glass thermometer |

ACTIVITY D

Tom is investigating the question 'how does the height of the top of the slope affect the time for a skateboard to go down the slope?'.

He uses the apparatus in the diagram below. He has a stopwatch to measure the time for the skateboard to get from start to finish.

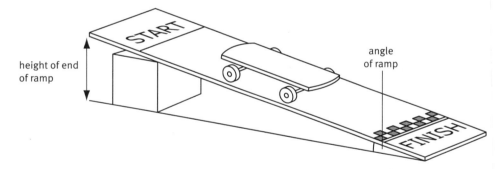

Tom wants to make his investigation as fair and reliable as possible.

✎ Write 'F' next to the things he could do to make the experiment **fairer**.

Write 'R' next to the things he could do to make the experiment **more reliable**.

Write 'FR' next to the things that would make the experiment both fairer **and** more reliable.

1. Measure time with light gates attached to a computer. _____

2. Make sure the skateboard is stationary at the start – do not push it! _____

3. Use the same skateboard each time. _____

4. Decide exactly where the finish line is. _____

5. Measure the height before and after each run to check that the slope has not moved. _____

6. Let the skateboard go down from each height three times. Measure the time each time and take an average. _____

ACTIVITY E

James is investigating the question 'how does temperature affect the speed that cress seedlings grow?'.

 Answer the questions.

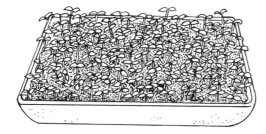

1. What factor will he change? This is the **independent variable**.

_____

2. What factor will he measure? This is the **dependent variable**.

_____

3. What measurements will he take?

_____

4. How will he make the experiment fair?

_____

_____

ACTIVITY F

Eva is investigating the question 'what factors affect the strength of an electromagnet?'.

She makes many predictions.

 Highlight or tick the statements below which are scientific predictions.

A The greater the number of coils, the weaker the electromagnet.

B The greater the number of coils, the more paper clips the electromagnet will pick up.

C I will need wire, an iron nail and a power pack to make an electromagnet.

D The electromagnet will be difficult to make.

E The smaller the current, the stronger the electromagnet.

F Putting an iron core in the electromagnet will make it stronger.

ACTIVITY G

 Draw lines to match each investigation with the best way of displaying the results. Draw **one** line from each investigation.

investigation

| how to display the results |

What are the numbers of left-handed and right-handed people in the class?

bar chart

What are the population sizes of different flower species in the field?

line graph

How does the temperature of a hot cup of coffee change over time?

How does the length of a developing fetus change with time?

pie chart

ACTIVITY H

Emebet did three investigations. Her results are in the tables. She displayed the results on graphs and pie charts, but did not label the axes.

 Use the tables to label the axes of the graphs and the segments of the pie chart. Don't forget to include units when you can!

smoking status	number of teachers
smoke now	10
used to smoke	20
have never smoked	40

student foot size	number of students
3–3.5	4
4–4.5	5
5–5.5	8
6–6.5	7
7–7.5	3
8–8.5	2

distance of planet from Sun, in million km	228	778	1430	2870	4500	5900
time for planet to orbit Sun, in Earth years	1.9	12	29	84	165	248

A

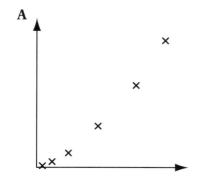

B

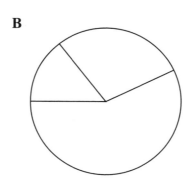

C

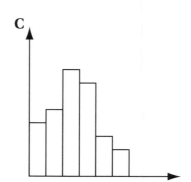

ACTIVITY I

Hassan and Sundara investigated the question 'is there a pattern in the way metals react with water?'. Their results are in the table.

name of metal	observation when we put the metal in water
sodium	Whizzed around on the surface of the water. Quickly made lots of bubbles.
iron	No change at first. After about a week, the surface of the iron had gone an orange-brown colour.
potassium	Whizzed around on the surface of the water. Quickly made lots of bubbles. Made a lilac-coloured flame.
lithium	Moved around slowly on the surface of the water. Made bubbles more slowly than potassium or sodium.

They made four conclusions.

 Next to each conclusion write down whether it is 'true', 'false', or you 'cannot tell'.

1. Potassium reacts more vigorously with water than sodium. _____

2. All metals react with water. _____

3. Of the metals we tried, iron is the least reactive with water. _____

4. Of the metals we tried, sodium is the most reactive with water. _____

ACTIVITY j

Tim and Alison did six investigations. They drew a graph for each investigation and made a conclusion from each graph.

Next to each conclusion write down whether it is 'true', 'false' or 'not sure'.

A 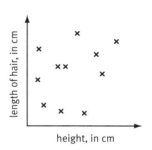 B 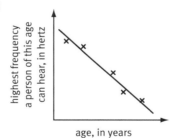 C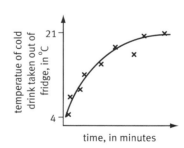

1. Graph A shows that tall students have longer hair. _____

2. Graph B shows that people can hear lower sounds as they get older. _____

3. Graph C shows that the room temperature was probably 21 °C. _____

Planning

Framing questions to investigate

When you do an investigation, identify something you want to find out about. Think of some ideas that you might be able to investigate. Then make up a scientific question that
o can be investigated scientifically
o will tell you what you want to know

For example, you want to find out about variation in humans. You think there might be relationships between height, foot size and hand size. One possible scientific question is 'do taller people have bigger feet?'.

Devising strategies

After you have made up a scientific question, you need to
o Think of some **strategies** you might use to answer the question. Choose one of these strategies.
o Do some **preliminary work** so that you can make a **prediction**.
o Identify the **independent variables**, the **dependent variables** and the **variables to control**.
o Decide what to **observe** or **measure**.
o Plan how to make your investigation as **safe** as possible.

For example, your scientific question is 'does the highest frequency people can hear decrease with age?'. One **strategy** is to measure the highest frequency you can hear every year until 2070. A better strategy is to test the hearing of 30 people of different ages – measure the highest frequency that each person can hear. To help you make a prediction, do some **preliminary work**. You could test three people of different ages or use a secondary source (a book or the internet). The **independent variable** is age. The **dependent variable** is the highest frequency each person can hear. Some **variables to control** are background noise, volume of the sound and previous hearing damage.

Choosing techniques and equipment

After you have devised your strategy, you need to choose techniques and equipment. For example, your scientific question is 'does the boiling point of salt solution increase as you put more salt in it?'. You must decide whether to use an alcohol-in-glass thermometer, a forehead thermometer or a temperature probe connected to a computer. You cannot use the forehead thermometer because its range is too small.

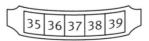
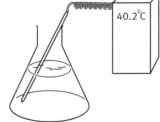

You also need to think about how **precise** your measurements need to be. You could measure the volume of water in a swimming pool to the nearest m^3. But you need to measure the volume of acid that neutralises one indigestion tablet to the nearest cm^3.

Sometimes you need to use **sampling techniques** to get information. For example, don't try to count all the daisies in a field – use a quadrat to estimate the number!

Collecting data

Decide the **range** of data to collect and the **number of measurements** in that range.

Make sure your data is as **reliable** as possible. You can do this by **repeating measurements** and taking readings of volume and temperature at **eye level**.

Obtaining and presenting evidence

Carry out your plan to get the evidence you need. Then decide how to present your data.

Presenting data

Present your data so that you can **process** it (if you need to) and so that you can see **patterns**.

If you know that you need to process your data, write down all your readings in a table. For example, your scientific question is 'which fuel makes the temperature of 50 cm³ of water increase the most?'. Your results table needs these four columns so that you can show how you worked out the temperature change:

fuel	temperature before heating, in °C	temperature after heating, in °C	temperature change, in °C

You can show the patterns in your data in a **table**, **pie chart**, **bar chart** or **line graph**. For example
○ Use a table to show the pattern in the reactions of metals with water.
○ Use a pie chart to show the numbers of people in your class who are left-handed or right-handed.
○ Use a bar chart if the independent variable is discontinuous, as shown below left.
○ Use a line graph if the independent variable is continuous, as shown below right.
Don't forget to use sensible **scales** on bar charts and line graphs. Include **units** every time you present data!

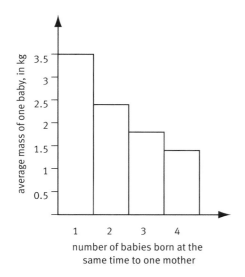

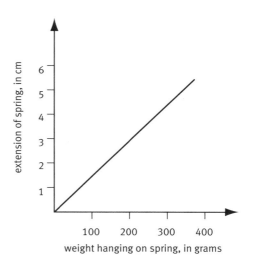

The number of babies born together at one time is the independent variable. It is discontinuous. The average mass of one baby is the dependent variable.

The weight hanging on the spring is the independent variable. It is continuous. The extension of the spring is the dependent variable.

Considering evidence
Identifying patterns and relationships

You can identify patterns from **graphs** or from **tables of data**.

substances you mix	observation
hydrochloric acid and calcium carbonate	bubbles – gas makes limewater cloudy
hydrochloric acid and sodium carbonate	bubbles – gas makes limewater cloudy
hydrochloric acid and copper carbonate	bubbles – gas makes limewater cloudy

This table shows a pattern – when hydrochloric acid reacts with certain metal carbonates, it gives off a gas that makes limewater cloudy.

This graph shows a pattern – in this experiment, the higher the temperature, the greater the mass of the solid that can dissolve.

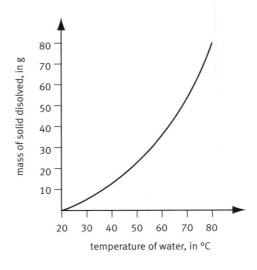

Using observations, measurements and data to draw conclusions

You can use your results to draw **conclusions**. Your conclusion may
○ **support** your original prediction or
○ **contradict** your original prediction or
○ not help you to decide

When you have a conclusion you can use it to predict more results.

For example, Tom set up this apparatus. His original prediction was 'the longer the piece of nichrome wire, the smaller the current in the circuit'.

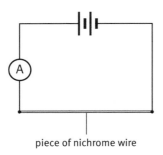

piece of nichrome wire

Tom's apparatus

Tom drew this graph from his results. From the pattern on the graph Tom could see that the current **depends on** the length of the wire. (Even though the current got smaller as the length got bigger, the current still depends on the length.)

Tom's conclusion was 'the longer the wire, the smaller the current'. His conclusion **supported** his original prediction. Tom used his conclusion to make some more predictions. He predicted the currents he would get at some lengths he hadn't tried.

Tom used his **scientific knowledge and understanding** to make another prediction. He knows that all metals conduct electricity. He predicted that his results would show a similar pattern if he used a zinc wire instead of a nichrome wire.

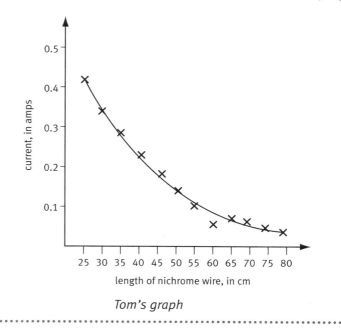

Tom's graph

Evaluating
Anomalous observations

Sometimes one or more results do not fit the pattern. These results appear to be wrong, or **anomalous**.

For example, one of the results on Tom's graph appears to be anomalous. Some reasons why it might be anomalous are
o he made a mistake in measuring the length of the wire
o he read the ammeter incorrectly
o the battery was running down

Does the evidence justify the conclusions?

In investigations you need to judge whether there is enough good evidence to support your conclusions.

For example, Debby measured the height of all the girls in her year 9 class. She found that they were all between 1.30 m and 1.60 m tall. She concluded that all 13- and 14-year-old girls are between 1.30 m and 1.60 m tall. The evidence **supports** this conclusion. However, the sample size is too small to **justify** the conclusion – there must be some 13- or 14-year-old girls in the world who are shorter than 1.30 m or taller than 1.60 m.

Suggesting improvements to investigations

You can usually improve an investigation!

You can improve **accuracy** by controlling anything that might influence your results. For example, draughts in the lab might affect temperature readings. Make sure you use the same thermometer to take all your readings in one experiment – even two thermometers that look the same might give you different results.

You can improve **reliability** by repeating measurements and by taking readings of temperature and volume at eye level.

CONCEPT MAP

Scientific enquiry

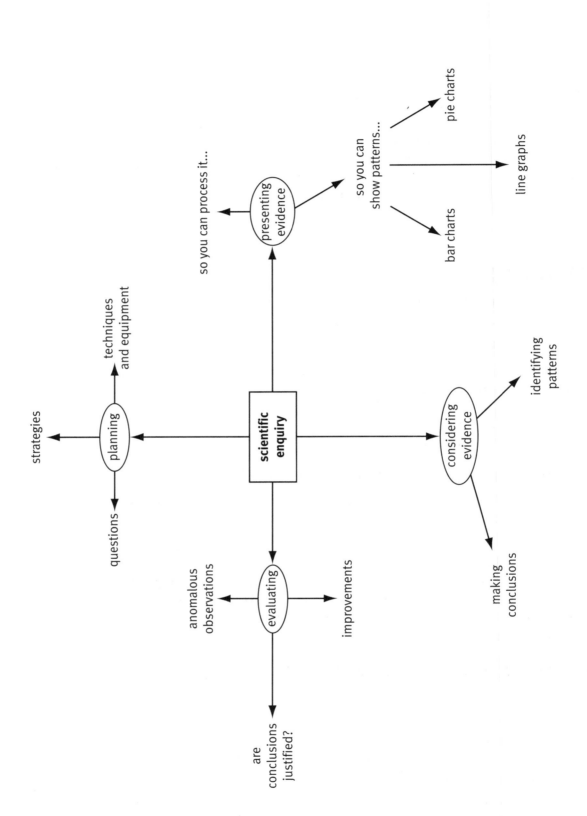

scientific enquiry

planning
- strategies
- questions
- techniques and equipment

presenting evidence
- so you can process it...
- so you can show patterns...
  - pie charts
  - line graphs
  - bar charts

considering evidence
- identifying patterns
- making conclusions

evaluating
- anomalous observations
- improvements
- are conclusions justified?

1. Charlotte and Tilly saw an advertisement claiming that Softy toilet tissue is more absorbent than any other type of toilet tissue.

They got three different types of toilet tissue. They counted the number of water drops absorbed by one piece of each type of toilet tissue.

They recorded their results in a table:

type of toilet tissue	number of drops one piece of the toilet tissue absorbed
Softy	40
Smooth	28
Drywell	33

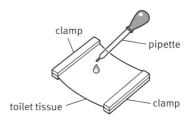

(a) They made a prediction. Which of these is not a prediction? Tick **one** box. *1 mark*

predictions

Softy will absorb more water than Drywell or Smooth. ☐

No brand will absorb more than 50 drops of water. ☐

Toilet tissue absorbs water because water is a liquid. ☐

Drywell will absorb the fewest drops. ☐

(b) Write down **one** thing they could do to make sure their investigation is fair. *1 mark*

_____

(c) They drew a bar chart of their results.
On the bar chart, draw a bar for Drywell. Use a ruler.
1 mark

(d) Charlotte and Tilly looked at their results and made conclusions.

Charlotte's conclusion was 'The claim in the advert is true. Softy is more absorbent than any other brand'.

Tilly's conclusion was 'We don't know if the advert is true. But Softy is more absorbent than Drywell and Smooth'.

Is Charlotte's or Tilly's conclusion better? Give a reason for your answer. *1 mark*

_____

_____

maximum 4 marks

2. Marcus and Liz investigated some young hawthorn trees. They used string and a ruler to measure the distance round the tree trunks. They used a ruler to measure the width of one leaf from each tree.

A hawthorn leaf

They recorded their results in a table.

distance round tree trunk (circumference), in mm	82	52	48	67	53
leaf width, in mm	38	22	20	30	25

(a) What question were they investigating?   *1 mark*

_____

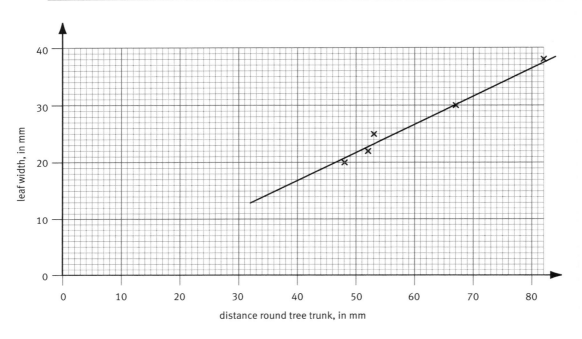

(b) They plotted their results on a graph.

    (i)   What conclusion can they make?   *1 mark*

    _____

    (ii) Liz measured the distance round the trunk (circumference) of another tree. It was 62 mm. Use the graph to predict the width of a leaf from this tree.   *1 mark*

    _____

(c) Marcus wants to make the results of the investigation more **reliable**. Suggest one improvement he can make to the way he collects his data.   *1 mark*

_____

_____

maximum 4 marks

3. Barney made an electrical cell from a lemon, a piece of copper and a piece of zinc. He wanted his cell to produce the highest voltage possible. He moved the copper and zinc so they were different distances apart, and measured the voltage for each distance.

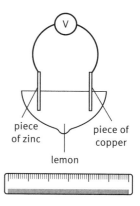

He predicted that 'the smaller the distance between the copper and zinc, the bigger the voltage'.

He used the apparatus opposite to test his prediction. He cleaned the copper and zinc after each reading.

(a) (i) Give the **one** factor Barney **changed** in this investigation.
(This is the independent variable.)

1 mark

_____

(ii) Give the factor Barney **examined** in this investigation.
(This is the dependent variable.)

1 mark

_____

(b) Barney plotted his results on a graph.

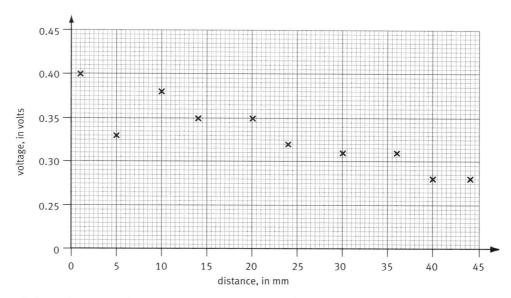

(i) One of the voltage readings appears to be wrong (anomalous).
Circle the anomalous result on the graph.

1 mark

(ii) Suggest one mistake Barney might have made to produce this anomalous result.

1 mark

_____

(iii) Draw a line of best fit on the graph.

1 mark

(iv) What conclusion can Barney make from his results?

1 mark

_____

maximum 6 marks

4. You have been asked to find out which breakfast cereal has the most energy stored in it: Oatcrunch, Ricecrackle or Wheatos.

You know that you can use a burning piece of cereal to heat up water. The cereal that stores the most energy will transfer the most heat energy to the water.

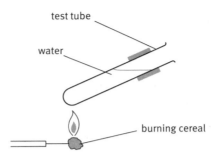

You can use whatever laboratory equipment you need, including
- measuring cylinders
- thermometers
- balance
- test tubes
- water
- matches

(a) (i) What factor would you examine to see which type of cereal stores the most energy? (This is the dependent variable.)   *1 mark*

_____

(ii) What equipment would you use to measure this dependent variable?   *1 mark*

_____

(b) (i) In the table, write headings in boxes **X** and **Y** to show what results you would record.   *2 marks*

(ii) Write a column heading in box **Z** to show how you would process your results.   *1 mark*

Type of cereal	X	Y	Z
Oatcrunch			
Ricecrackle			
Wheatos			

(c) Suggest two factors you would control to make your investigation fair.   *2 marks*

_____

_____

maximum 7 marks

Answers to questions

Cells:Workout

Activity A

nutrient	what the body uses the nutrient for	foods that contain the nutrient	enzyme that breaks down molecules of the nutrient
protein	growth and repair of tissues	meat, fish, cheese, milk, eggs, beans	protease
carbohydrates	energy	potatoes, rice, pasta, bread, cereal	amylase
fats	storing energy	butter, cooking oil, chips	lipase
vitamins and minerals	for chemical reactions in the body	fruit and vegetables, cereal, milk (calcium), red meat (iron)	not broken down
fibre	to help everything move round the digestive system	fruit vegetables cereal wholemeal bread	not broken down

Activity B
Smoking – heart, lungs; eating too much fatty food – heart; drinking too much alcohol – liver, brain; not taking enough exercise – heart; taking ecstasy – brain

Activity C
P – sperm duct; **Q** – urethra; **R** – penis; **S** – testis; **T** – scrotum

Activity D
Substances that pass from mother to embryo – oxygen, nutrients, antibodies, alcohol, some viruses, nicotine

Substances that pass from embryo to mother – waste products, carbon dioxide

Activity E
1. T   2. F   3. T   4. F   5. T   6. F   7. T
8. T   9. T   10. T

Activity F
Fungi; protein; yeast; virus; bacteria; transmitted; salmonella; immunisation; vaccine; antibodies; antibodies

Activity G
Pollen cell – fertilises egg cell in plant – small and light; egg cell (ovum) – carries genetic information from mother to offspring – contains food store; epithelial cell – protects surfaces of organs – produces lubricating liquids; red blood cell – carries oxygen – large surface area; nerve cell – transmits messages – conducts electrical signals

Activity H
R, P, S, Q

Activity I
1. Chicken   2. Red ants   3. 250 g   4. 933 g

Cells: Practice for SATs

Question 1
(a)(i) Chloroplast; vacuole
   (ii) Cell membrane – controls what goes in and out of the cell; cell wall – supports the cell; nucleus – controls what the cell does; cytoplasm – chemical reactions happen here
(b)Tissues; organs

Question 2
(a)(i) Ovary (ii) Every 28 days
   (iii) Lining of uterus (womb)
(b)   (i) Sperm and ovum (egg) (ii) Oviduct (fallopian tube)
(c)(i) One of: oxygen; antibodies
   (ii) Two of: viruses; nicotine; alcohol; drugs

Question 3
(a)(i) Growth and repair of tissues (ii) 16.8 g
   (iii) Heart (iv) 545 g or 546 g
(b)(i) Protein – protease; starch – amylase; fat – lipase
   (ii) Protein, carbohydrate and fat molecules are too big to get through the walls of the gut **or** the molecules are too big to get into cells.

Question 4
(a)They have a large surface area to absorb water and minerals **or** they have thin walls so that water and minerals can get into the cell.
(b)They contain many chloroplasts where photosynthesis takes place **and** the cell walls are transparent so that sunlight can reach the chloroplasts.
(c)Carbon dioxide + water $\longrightarrow$ glucose + oxygen

(d)(i) Two of: movement; respiration; reproduction; excretion; nutrition
(ii) Carbon dioxide and water
(iii) Plants need light to photosynthesise – this is not usually available at night. They do not need light to respire.

Interdependence: Workout

Activity A
Producers – wheat, lettuce; predators – fox, badger, frog, beetle, mouse; primary consumers – slug, mouse; prey animals – slug, frog, mouse, beetle; herbivore – slug

Activity B
Decrease; increase; compete; decreases

Activity C
X2C, X3H, X3I, X4J, X5H, X7D, X8D, X9E, Y1B, Y1G, Y4F, Y6A, Y7B, Y8B, Y9E

Activity D
Plants make their own food by photosynthesis; **flowering plants** make seeds in flowers; **conifers** make seeds in cones, e.g. fir tree; **mosses and liverworts** have simple leaves; **dicotyledons** broad leaves with branched veins, flowers often brightly coloured, e.g. rose; **monocotyledons** narrow leaves with parallel veins, e.g. grasses; **ferns** have roots, e.g. tree fern

Activity E

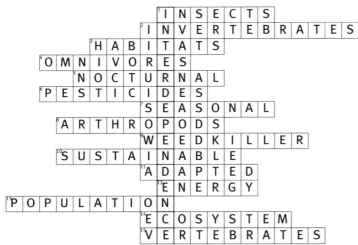

Answer 9 could also be herbicides.

Activity F
Weeds – crops – light, space, soil nutrients, water; pests – humans – food

Activity G
Add weedkiller – pyramid B; add pesticide – pyramid C; add pesticide and weedkiller – pyramid A

Interdependence: Practice for SATs

Question 1
(a) Whale; shark; cod; newt
(b) Shark; cod
(c) Spider; grasshopper

Question 2
(a) Two of: good stamina – they have to work for long hours; calm – they may be faced with crowds of noisy people; brave – they may have to enter frightening situations
(b) Inherited – eye colour, colour; environmental – tail docked short or natural length; both – mass, number of instructions it understands

Question 3
(a)(i) One of: grass; acacia tree (ii) One of: lion; wild dog
(iii) One of: giraffe; impala; zebra; wildebeest
(iv) One of: giraffe; impala; zebra; wildebeest
(b) Acacia tree $\rightarrow$ giraffe $\rightarrow$ lion
(c) There is not enough water or grass where they are. They migrate to areas where there is enough water or grass.
(d)(i) When the zebra eats grass, energy is transferred from the grass to the zebra. Some of this energy is transferred to the lion when the lion eats the zebra.
(ii) The Sun

Question 4
(a) It has a sharp hooked beak for tearing at the flesh of dead cows.
(b)
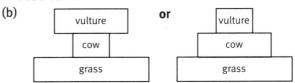
(c) (i) When vultures eat a dead cow that has been given diclofenac, the drug gets into their bodies. When vultures eat more dead cows, the drug accumulates in their bodies – it is not excreted.
(ii) Increase (**or** decrease)
(iii) The food web shows that wild dogs compete with vultures for food (dead cows). If there are fewer vultures eating cows, there are more dead cows available for wild dogs to eat. (**Or** the wild dog population may fall if they are also affected by the drug.)

Particles: Workout

Activity B
IF YOU KNOW Al YOU CaN BOTh KISS

Activity C
Elements – gold, chlorine, silver, silicon, sodium, potassium; compounds – three of: sulphur dioxide, sodium chloride, iron oxide, water; sedimentary rock – sandstone; metals – gold, silver, potassium, sodium; non-metal elements – chlorine, silicon; oxides – two of: sulphur dioxide, water, iron oxide; metamorphic rock – marble

Activity D
P – a pure compound; **Q** – a mixture of two elements; **R** – a pure element; **S** – a mixture of two compounds

Activity E
1. P   2. C   3. C   4. C   5. P   6. P   7. P

Activity F
A – 4; B – 5; C – 1; D – 6; E – 2; F – 3

Activity G

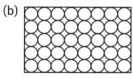

A crossword puzzle with the following answers:
1. CONDENSES
2. HYDROXIDE
3. FREEZES
4. ONE
5. CELL MEMBRANES
6. DISTILLATION
7. WATER
8. BOILING
9. MELTING
10. FILTRATION
11. ACID
12. EVAPORATE
13. HYDROGEN
14. ELECTROLYSIS

Activity H

1. 4   2. 8   3. 1   4. norepinephrine

Activity I

2. Iron + sulphur $\longrightarrow$ iron sulphide; Fe + S $\longrightarrow$ FeS
3. Limestone $\longrightarrow$ calcium oxide + carbon dioxide;
   $CaCO_3 \longrightarrow CaO + CO_2$
4. Sodium hydroxide + hydrochloric acid $\longrightarrow$ sodium chloride + water; $NaOH + HCl \longrightarrow NaCl + H_2O$
5. Methane + oxygen $\longrightarrow$ carbon dioxide + water;
   $CH_4 + 2O_2 \longrightarrow CO_2 + 2H_2O$
6. Copper oxide + nitric acid $\longrightarrow$ copper nitrate + water;
   $CuO + 2HNO_3 \longrightarrow Cu(NO_3)_2 + H_2O$
7. Potassium + water $\longrightarrow$ potassium hydroxide + hydrogen;
   $2K + 2H_2O \longrightarrow 2KOH + H_2$
8. Aluminium + iron oxide $\longrightarrow$ aluminium oxide + iron;
   $2Al + 3FeO \longrightarrow Al_2O_3 + 3Fe$

Particles: Practice for SATs

Question 1

(a)(i) Sugar cane (ii) Cranberry
(b)(i) Green (ii) An acid

Question 2

(a)(i) It does not react with water or acids
   (ii) It conducts heat and it conducts electricity
(b)

 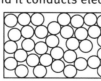

solid   liquid

(c)(i) 2996 ºC (ii) Solid

Question 3

(a) An element
(b)(i) The gold ring reacts most slowly with oxygen from the air. (ii) Iron (iii) Hydrogen
(c) Water and oxygen
(d) Copper + oxygen $\longrightarrow$ copper oxide

Question 4

(a)(i) Carbon and hydrogen (ii) 11
(b)(i) Carbon dioxide and water
   (ii) The limewater goes cloudy.
   (iii) To make steam condense into liquid water
(c) Two of: climate change; sea level rises; icecaps melt

Forces: Workout

Activity A

A – it is summer in the southern hemisphere; B – an eclipse of the Sun; C – a full moon; D – it is summer in the northern hemisphere; E – an eclipse of the Moon

Activity C

1. F   2. T   3. F   4. F   5. T   6. T   7. F
8. F   9. T   10. F   11. T   12. F   13. T   14. T
15. T   16. F   17. F   18. T

Activity D

1. A   2. B   3. B   4. A   5. B

Activity E

David could move nearer the pivot; Victoria could move away from the pivot.

Activity F

1. D   2. A   3. B   4. A   5. A   6. A   7. C

Forces: Practice for SATs

Question 1

(a) A and C
(b) A – upthrust force; B – water resistance; C – weight; D – forward force
(c) Water resistance slows it down.

Question 2

(a)(i) Two of: iron; steel; cobalt; nickel (ii) Friction
   (iii) Steel
(b)(i) Diagram to show **either** the magnet floating on water **or** the magnet suspended from a piece of string that is free to move
   (ii) One of: to get pieces of magnetic metals out of the eye; to close cupboard doors; on noticeboards; fridge magnets

(c)

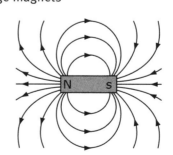

Question 3

(a) Gravity

(b)(i) Sedna

(ii) One of: Sedna has a larger orbit; Sedna has further to travel; Sedna travels more slowly.

(iii) Sedna and Pluto are further away from the Sun than the other planets.

(c) Light rays from the Sun hit Sedna. Sedna reflects some of this light towards Earth.

Question 4

(a) Speed = distance ÷ time = 100 m ÷ 10 s = 10 m/s

(b)(i) Air resistance **or** drag

(ii) When he is more streamlined fewer particles oppose him as he moves forward.

(c)(i) The athlete is running at a steady speed.

(ii) The athlete is speeding up **or** accelerating.

Energy: Workout

Activity A

1. One of the cells is the wrong way round.

2. This is not a complete circuit (the wire is not joined to one of the cells).

3. The voltmeter should be connected in parallel to one of the components (not in series).

4. The ammeter should be connected in series (not in parallel with the buzzer).

Activity B

Components; energy; chemical; transformed; potential; volts; sound; kinetic; smaller

Activity C

Burn a fossil fuel, for example coal, oil or gas. Burn a biofuel like methane. Use a windmill to 'collect' energy from the wind or a tidal barrage to 'collect' energy from tides. Heat up water to make steam. Make the turbine turn. Make the generator turn. You have generated electricity!

Activity D

Convection and conduction need particles; radiation does not.

Conduction happens best in solids; convection happens best in liquids and gases.

Activity E

A 100 °C B 0 °C C 20 °C D 37 °C E 4 °C F −18 °C
G −89 °C H 58 °C I 1064 °C J −210 °C K 1000 °C L −150 °C

Activity H

1. Strawberries look red in red light because they reflect red light.

2. Strawberries look red in white light because they reflect red light and absorb all the other colours.

3. Strawberries look black in blue light because they absorb blue light. There is no red light to reflect.

4. Peas look green in white light because they reflect green light and absorb the other colours.

5. Peas look black in red light because they absorb red light and there is no green light to reflect.

Energy: Practice for SATs

Question 1

(a)(i) Parallel (ii) It will stay on.

(b)(i) The car battery (ii) Electrical; heat and light (last two can be in either order)

(c) The current at P is the same as the current at Q; the current at Q is bigger than the current at S.

Question 2

(a)

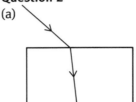

(b) Prism – dispersion; glass block – refraction; mirror – reflection

Question 3

(a) Coal-fired power station – can generate electricity all the time – produces a gas that makes acid rain; wind turbines – does not make gases that pollute the atmosphere – cannot generate electricity all the time; methane gas power station – makes good use of waste materials – relies on people making enough rubbish.

(b) Two of: wave power; tidal power; solar power; geothermal power

(c) Chemical; heat or thermal; kinetic

Question 4

(a)(i) Finan and Woody (ii) C, E, A, B, D, F

(b)(i) X (ii) W (iii) W (iv) W

Scientific enquiry: Workout

Activity A

Which type of indigestion tablet neutralises most acid?

Does deodorant cause breast cancer?

At the bottom of which British swimming pool is the pressure highest?

Does food go mouldy quicker in a cold room or a hot room?

Activity B

Is there a relationship between the length of a slug and its mass?

Does the height of the first bounce of a football depend on the height we drop it from?

Is there a relationship between the height of a plant and the pH of rainwater?

Activity C

Measuring cylinder; stopwatch; stirring rod; beaker; temperature probe **or** glass thermometer; kettle; balance

Activity D

1. R   2. F   3. F
4. FR   5. R   6. R

Activity E

1. Temperature

2. Height of cress seedlings

3. Height of cress seedlings at regular intervals (e.g. every 2 days)

4. Keep all conditions (except for temperature) the same (e.g. same amount of light and water).

Activity F

A; B; E; F

Activity G

Bar chart – what are the population sizes of different flower species in the field?

Line graph – how does the temperature of a hot cup of coffee change over time? How does the length of a developing fetus change with time?

Pie chart – what are the numbers of left-handed and right-handed people in the class?

Activity H

A – planet distances and orbit times;
B – smoking status;
C – student foot sizes

Activity I

1. True
2. Cannot tell
3. True
4. False

Activity J

1. False
2. Not sure – the graph shows nothing about the lowest frequency, only the highest!
3. True

Scientific enquiry: Practice for SATs

Question 1

(a) Toilet tissue absorbs water because water is a liquid.

(b) One of: use pieces of toilet paper of the same size; make sure the drips are of roughly equal volume

(c) Bar drawn up to 33 drops

(d) Tilly's conclusion is better – as they have only tested three brands of toilet paper, they cannot tell whether Softy is the most absorbent brand of all brands that there are.

Question 2

(a) Is there a relationship between the circumference of the trunk of a hawthorn tree and the width of a leaf from the tree?
(b)(i) The bigger a hawthorn tree's trunk circumference, the wider the leaf.
(ii) About 27 mm
(c) He could measure the widths of three leaves from each tree. He could use these results to calculate an average for each tree.

Question 3

(a)(i) The distance between the piece of copper and the piece of zinc
(ii) The voltage
(b)(ii) One of: he might have measured the distance between the pieces of metal incorrectly; he might have misread the reading on the voltmeter; he might not have forgotten to clean the pieces of metal before the reading.
(iv) The greater the distance between the two pieces of metal, the smaller the voltage.

Question 4

(a)(i) The temperature rise of the water
(ii) A thermometer **or** a temperature probe connected to a computer
(b)(i) X – temperature of water before heating, in °C;
Y – temperature of water after heating, in °C
(ii) Temperature change, in °C
(c) Use the same volume of water each time; burn the same mass of cereal each time.